There Are No Accidents

There Are No Accidents

by jerry stocking

To correspond with Jerry Stocking
or to find out about other products offered by
Moose Ear Press or A Choice Experience, Inc.
see the last five pages of this book.

Editor: Sara Stamy
Copy Editor: Jackie Stocking
Proofreader: Karen Bates
Cover design and art work: Jerry Stocking

Thank you to all of the people who read the manuscript or
aided in the production of
There Are No Accidents.

Published by
Moose Ear Press
First Printing 1995

ISBN: 0-9629593-3-2

Dedication

To mountains, to mole hills, and to all of the fantastic terrain in between.

———————

Introduction

There was once a little mouse who knew everything. She knew holes in the ground. She knew the smells of food and the tastes of all the plants that were good to eat. There was usually enough to eat, and little to remember. She lived in a forest glen seldom disturbed by creatures larger than herself. At the first sign of anything unusual, the mouse would scuttle down her hole to hide. She would wait in her tiny warm space, near her reserves of food, until she remembered there was a world to explore outside. What more was there, what more could there possibly be? She always knew what to do. There was no right or wrong. Just living.

One day, as she was sniffing out a succulent cluster of acorns, she had a feeling she was being watched. She started to shake and run. First toward her hole, then toward the acorns. Something was wrong. She didn't know what.

Above her, far above, loomed a creature giant by her standards. Regal white head and black wings floating on the wind currents, the eagle looked down. His world was huge. It included tens of miles, every little beast within his view, the clouds, the hills, the rivers, and the treetops. Sometimes he would hunt, like now, but often he would just lock his wings in position and soar for soaring's sake, or sit at the top of the tallest tree in the forest. Whatever he could see was his, and right now he could see a mouse far below. Tucking his wings in, he dropped like a stone toward his lunch.

On the edge of the woods, a young boy and girl had interrupted their game of follow-the-leader to watch the eagle soar. They saw him begin the dive. They couldn't see the mouse yet, but they knew from experience that the eagle was on his way toward some small creature on the ground. Down went the bird, claws extended, braking at the last moment, then rising again. Taking the mouse for her last ride. The children watched with mixed emotions, not knowing whether to cheer for the eagle or mourn for the mouse, a dilemma neither the eagle nor the mouse could entertain.

Wiggling wildly, Mistress Mouse freed herself and fell unhurt, but badly shaken, to the ground. The eagle never looked back. The mouse ran for her hole as fast as she could. The children clapped, jumping up and down.

Racing home, they told their parents the story. First from their own perspective, their suspense as they watched the eagle dive, then from the precarious position of Mistress Mouse, and finally as the eagle with—and then suddenly without—lunch.

The stories were all different. To the mouse, it was a life-threatening attack, confusing and confounding. To the eagle, it was a lost snack, forgotten as he circled again and performed a successful dive. To the children, it was entertainment, excitement, and education.

This and many other stories made up their childhoods, influencing their lives as adults. Mice and eagles do what they do well, but they cannot tell stories. They cannot observe from beyond their own worlds and experiences, nor can they imagine or be entertained. People can adopt different perceptives, and by doing so live in a limitless world. They can concoct incredible stories to entertain, to expand their own lives and those of everyone they contact.

Living life with wonderful stories leads to a wonderful life. We are all story-tellers. What follows is a story I hope will entertain and enrich your life.

If something happens once it can be called an accident. If it happens twice, it can be ignored as a philosophy. If it happens often, it magically becomes a scientific fact and oppresses almost everybody. The only time anything becomes persistent is when we continue to ignore it. If we attend to apparent accidents the first time we can avoid philosophy and science and be amusingly entertained all the time.

When the strange woman, beaming with recognition, rushed through the departing plane passengers to give Paul an exuberant bear hug, he thought it was an accident. "Benny!" Her eyes gleamed.

He could only stare. The air at 8,000 feet was thin, he was panting and lightheaded, and maybe the woman was a hallucination. But she was certainly a realistic one. Paul might have seen this woman before, he could not be sure. Her abundant light gray hair contradicted her youthful features, confusing the whole issue of chronological age. She was dressed in a nondescript black knit outfit and would have been entirely forgettable if it were not for a certain sparkle in her eye and her bizarre greeting. She continued to hug him tightly.

"Benny," she repeated. "Oh, Benny, I've missed you so much, where have you been?" She stretched out the last word in a monotone whine, "beeeeeeeeeen."

She wouldn't let go. Paul had a weird, panicky feeling she never would. He cleared his throat. "I'm not Benny."

The woman pulled back, looked him in the face. The eager light in her eyes faded. "And so you aren't. I just keep jumping my cues. Perhaps it is a lifetime too early." She turned and was gone.

Paul stood swaying and blinking dizzily. Somehow yanked out of time and place, wondering if it had happened at all. He looked around for a witness, but the other disembarking passengers had hurriedly left the chilly mountain airstrip for the shelter of the small terminal.

A physical shrug can dismiss most "accidents." Not this one. A chance meeting, a misidentification? Would they meet again? If so, would he be ready for her? He hadn't received that many hugs from women who weren't aunts or cousins…. Not knowing how to mentally shrug, he let it go. The woman was gone, for now. There was nothing to do but claim his luggage, find the university and his dorm room.

Years later, his odd welcome at the airport would appear one of the more ordinary events of his freshman year. Now, shaking his head, he made his way to the shelves they called a baggage claim, half expecting to meet the hug-prone woman again. No sign of her.

Paul was relieved to see his luggage, reassuringly familiar. He'd packed light—hitchhiking across the country the summer before had taught him that. The ratio of pencils and notebooks to camping equipment in his bags revealed his freshman focus.

Stepping out of the terminal into the crisp, thin morning air, he took a deep breath and gazed over the Gunnison Valley. The mountains were much as he had pictured them, but bigger.

It was an inevitable chance meeting. He was young, though his face was so weathered it was hard to see his youth. As the Wright Brothers still worked on a new invention in Kitty Hawk, he arrived in Gunnison on foot to make his fortune. He could have stayed back east, comfortable, earning his keep and a bit more. That was not for him. He wanted the gold, the quick rich waiting in

these mountains. Thus far he had done a lot of digging, and some panning, but had found no gold. Hands callused, he continued to work, bound and determined to find the gold.

The chance meeting was an interruption in his digging. This day he had begun work in a small rock formation, alternately picking and shoveling. He had worked for several hours when he sensed that he was not alone. He had company, uninvited company, a threat to his would-be fortune, perhaps. He turned slowly, tensed for a fight. All thoughts of threat disappeared. The visitor was an ancient Indian. He sat still, so still it seemed he might not even be alive. He looked to be as old as the rock he leaned against.

Ben approached his visitor cautiously. He noticed a pale light, a glow in the Indian's eyes that betrayed his stillness. Yes, he was alive, very much alive, though breathing very little. Silently the Indian requested silence, and so effectively that the miner sat cross-legged about five feet from him. An hour passed. Two went by, time enough for even Ben to experience social discomfort, peacefulness, and finally physical discomfort. Well over three hours went by. Gracefully, the Indian rose, loped off with the ease of a coyote. His movements were not of a man his age.

Ben rose with all the ease of a very old, stiff man. He didn't know what to think—indeed it was several minutes before he could think at all. Just being in the pres-

ence of this old sage had cleared his mind entirely, and he had to reassemble his old thoughts even to remember who he was. The ancient Indian had taken him on a journey. Where, he could not yet know, but he had conveyed a message to Ben. This Ben realized three days later, in a moment of revelation. He began digging where the Indian had been sitting, and within minutes hit one of the largest veins of gold ever found in the Rockies.

Paul had looked forward to Colorado for a long time. He was young and eager, and not about to let the odd scene at the airport dampen his arrival. He was going to college to get the kind of education that required a sleeping bag, lantern, camp stove, waterproof matches, and the great outdoors.

It was a short and pleasant walk to downtown Gunnison where it was still so early that all the stores remained closed. This town was not a suburb to anywhere, it was a town in its own right. From the old-time hardware store, one peek in the window revealing an endless and uninventoried array of paraphernalia, to the ornate bank building that reminded Paul of something from an old Western movie, this town was full of personality. There was a cigar store Indian and a genuine barber pole along with wooden benches that Paul imagined might soon be filled with old-timers, the keepers of stories from Gunnison's earlier days. Paul stepped back in history even

setting foot in the town, and appreciated the irony of coming to such a place to educate himself for his future.

The university itself had very little personality—a
collection of red brick buildings with white mortar. The
only sign of earlier times was one adobe, three-story dormitory. A building that Paul would live in for the next
eight months but never call home.

Dropping his luggage off at his assigned room, he
found nothing to convince him to linger at the dorm. He
walked around the campus. Behind the football stadium,
the grass hills they called a stadium, a mountain rose. It
wasn't the biggest around, but he'd heard the football team
ran up it for training. This was the school for Paul. Running up a mountain at this altitude was something he
wanted to imagine. That first day, the three flights of stairs
to his dorm room were taxing enough. Later, climbing
those stairs would be as easy as a stroll in the park.

Sports had not been important to him, although he
had played tennis and wrestled in high school. He considered himself to be in good shape from doing a lot of walking his senior year in high school. As each school day
ended, his day of walking the family dog and reading had
begun. Paul would read until sunset while walking with
Hush, the 105-pound result of a moment of pleasure between a Golden Retriever and an Alaskan Malamute.
Existentialism was the subject of the first half of his senior
year, and plays, primarily surrealistic, consumed the second half. Hush didn't seem to mind his reading as long as

they continued to walk. Neither Sartre or Camus would have fit in well at his high school, and neither did Paul.

While his peers were busy with clubs, work, or intermurals after school, Paul and Hush were busy becoming a common sight in the suburbs. Soon they were recognized by everyone in town as "that big dog and the guy reading." His father used to tell him to make sure to be remembered for something. It is doubtful we get to choose what we are remembered for.

Miles of walking had gotten Paul into what he thought was fair physical shape, though ambling along suburban sidewalks bears little resemblance to the hiking he would be doing in the mountains. Reading for several hours a day had been preparing him mentally. Ever the optimist, Paul was ready to explore the mountains.

He had four days before classes began. He planned to go camping, but that was the only plan. His goal was simply to walk any direction and find out where he ended up. The mountains around Gunnison have no street signs—most don't even have names—so getting lost was the easiest part.

Leaving the university, Paul headed southeast. This direction took him through town for supplies: a loaf of bread, some canned beans and two pounds of potatoes. He left "civilization" behind to the northwest ignoring roads and hiking cross-country. These were old mountains. They were not the dramatic pointed variety found further north around Rocky Mountain National Park. But their age made them a bit more inviting if weathered. They demanded wandering and were impressive by their lack of distinction. There were no landmarks here, just mountain after nondescript mountain, each weathered to the point of smoothness.

His route took him, within a half mile, to the Gunnison River—a shallow, cold, fast-moving knife cutting easily through the old rock. It looked small enough, but what it lacked in size it made up in ferocity and temperature. He either had to wade across it or go upriver to search for an easy crossing. Optimism chose the cold path. He waded the freezing river with new boots strung over his shoulder. Within moments his feet were numb.

There is something very real and intimate about crossing a wide, cold, fast-moving mountain stream in bare feet. Paul remembered cowboy movies where the wagon trains and herds of cattle made their way across just such streams. The movie seemed real until he set foot in this stream. In the movie, the stream had looked cold; this water *was* cold.

Years later, he could still clearly recall the intensity of the cold water. Growing up in the suburbs had been like living a theoretical life. Paul knew how cold streams were, but had not felt many. He knew what big mountains were, but had not climbed them. He knew how romantic it would be to sleep out under the wide open skies with billions of stars to watch….He knew so much and had done so little. The difference between knowing and doing was something he only knew about.

He had seen hundreds of people killed or maimed on television or in movies, but his life had never really been threatened. He had never broken a bone and had only had stitches once, in his right index finger, courtesy of a mishap with an ax. His idea of pain was the congestion accompanying a cold or the dull soreness the day after a hard run.

This water was cold and the hard, pointed rocks did not care about Paul's tender feet. He slipped once, splashing his left side all the way up to the hip. He managed crossing without further incident. Proud of his success, he looked back to discover the bread had fallen from his pack and was floating away. It would be beans and potatoes for the next four days.

It was only an accident, losing the bread. From Paul's perspective the whole world was composed of accidents. If his high school physics had been a bit more practical, he would have realized one of the primary rules of the universe: *there are no accidents.*

The bread was packed in a particular way so that when Paul slipped, the jolt would be just enough to contribute the bread to the river. In addition, this brand of bread was just the right weight and packaging for it to easily slide from his pack. The company had designed just the right product for him to drop that day. Years

earlier, Paul would have laughed at attributing too much meaning to a silly coincidence.

In an effort to turn what could be an important moment into a light one, he waved to the bread and shouted, "Good-bye." He pictured possible scenarios for the final resting place of the bread: in a bear's belly, at the edge of a dam, or wedged in an eddy near a large cliff always at the point of almost going over the falls only to circle again endlessly. Perhaps someone would find the bread who needed it more than he did and be provided the nourishment to make it back to civilization. Paul did not know what would happen to the bread, a fact that only encouraged entertaining speculation.

Paul worked his socks on over his damp feet and pulled on his boots. Ahead of him was the foothill of a barren, rocky mountain. Braced for his first climb, he began.

The rocks were well-weathered, dangerous in that some were secure while others would give way underfoot. To an eagle, the climb would have looked silly. Small rocks fell every which way behind him as he repeatedly lost and regained his balance. No, this was not much like streets and sidewalks. Occasionally, while walking in the suburbs, he'd played a game. He would close his eyes and continue walking on blind trust. Knowing when he was nearing a curb, hearing a car approaching, were easy. Here in the mountains, closing his eyes while walking might mean his death.

It took an hour to climb the first hill, he estimated. One rule he had was no timepieces on a campout. His blue work shirt was soaked with sweat, and his feet had gone from freezing cold to warm. From Paul's vantage point, he wasn't high enough to see the whole town, but the dormitory and other tall buildings rose beyond the foothills nestling Gunnison. Paul had arrived in Gunnison just the day before and was already leaving it.

Pausing occasionally to rub the tiredness from his legs, Paul climbed all afternoon. The land was barren. Much of his energy was spent reassessing the kind of shape he was in and lamenting the loss of the bread. The days are long in open spaces, and he climbed until the afternoon light dwindled into dusk. Gunnison was no longer visible. His canteen was running low and the river was the only water he had seen all day. The land was dry, beaten, and weathered, three adjectives that seemed to apply even more to Paul.

Darkness set in long after tiredness. There was no wood around and he had so little energy that a fire seemed unnecessary. He ate a dinner of cold beans, and spread his foam mat and sleeping bag on a fairly smooth piece of ground. It felt like Heaven just to lie down, stretch, close his eyes and relax.

Paul looked up. There had never been this many stars before. Silence reigned.

Just as he was dozing off to a well-earned sleep, reliving his first day's hike, an earsplitting "bang" shat-

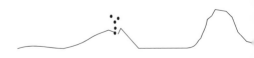

tered the calm. Like thunder, but not at a distance. Personal thunder. He couldn't think. Was the noise from within or outside of him? Deafened, Paul cowered as rock chips and dust showered down upon him.

For a fraction of a second Paul thought he was dreaming. "Help!" resounded in his head, never made it past his lips. "Death comes unexpectedly," he recalled a minister once saying, but until now he hadn't appreciated how fast it could come. Paul hovered at the brink between life and death, crossing over and back, finally falling to the side of the living. Barely. He lay stunned. The shower of rocks continued to fall on him. Not big rocks, fragments exploding from the ledge less than two feet above his head.

Here was his second moment knocked senseless since arriving in Gunnison. Intensely confused, he was falling with no rational thought to catch him, no logic and

no help. He could only breathe, and wait for his wits to return.

He was no longer tired, being tired took perspective and at this moment he had none. He would not be even fully confused for a few seconds. A gap had opened in the mountains of his thought, a valley not of peace and restfulness but of nothing. Paul was not in the mountains; he simply did not exist at all. Nothing that defined him remained in that moment, and without a definition there is no meaning, without meaning there is no personal existence. Short-lived as this moment was, it would remain infinitely memorable.

Within seconds, fear and confusion rushed in. He needed to make sense of what had just happened. He saw a flash of lights, heard the sound of a pickup truck motor far below him. Two more shots rang out.

He understood what had happened. There were some locals out shining deer and shooting at them. They had no idea that he was there, nor would they probably have cared. The bullet had missed the deer and flown above his head, accidentally. A chill ran down his spine when he realized that moments before the shot, he had been kneeling beside his bed roll, his head directly in the path of their bullet.

This was the closest he had come to dying since he was three years old and stuck a bus token up his nose.

This brush with death left him stunned and scared: not scared of another bullet, that was unlikely enough, but scared of how close death is at every moment. How the difference between life and death is one breath or lack of breath away.

Paul didn't sleep much that night. There was little reprieve from the recurring dream of his death. He died in many ways, but in the end death was always the same. The only life he had in the dream was just before the moment of death, always at the edge, leaning, ready to fall, but something needed to push him over the edge. He could not fall on his own. Faintly, he discerned unrecognizable shapes that continued to slip by behind him, able to push, ready to push, but it was apparently not yet his time to die. It was a long night.

Years later, he would report that he had still not left the edge. None of us ever do.

His best sleep came as the dark was slowly chased away, just before sunrise. He missed the first rays of the sun, and woke oddly reluctant to leave the dream world. The dream of death held him, and a surprisingly big chunk of it carried over into his waking state. He awoke to the sight of new, unweathered rock where the bullet had made a five inch diameter gouge in the rocky ledge above him. His sleeping bag was covered with rock chips and dust. As he brushed off the debris, he picked up two of the larger chips of rock and slipped them into his pocket—souvenirs of the brush with death. Months later he would find another use for them.

Well rested he was not. He felt a pressure on his forehead and tightness in his tired eyes. The dull ache in his head fit the description of hang-overs he had heard about but never experienced. He moved in slow motion, trying to focus. He was still moving much faster than the mountains but slower than usual. He wouldn't find out until later that this is what life is like living in the moment. When the past and future disappear, the present is still and entirely manageable—and even more important than that, enjoyable.

In no hurry to be on his way, Paul shook out his sleeping bag and lay back down on it. He became aware of the weight of his body pressing against the ground. Spontaneously his first meditation began. His eyelids slid closed. His eyes moved rapidly behind them, seeing deep within his memories.

He was trapped. It was as though he was caught in a body too small to contain the energy surging in him. He must get bigger or be crushed. Now he felt the rock all around him. The rock was crushing him. The cave-in had taken less than five seconds and here he was trapped. One arm was pinned down at his side and the other smashed up against the side of his face. The pressure precluded any pain, a bit like a body cast. If he stayed in this position long enough it would set any broken bones

he might have, but might cement his future as a fossil as well.

All of this for the gold. He hadn't realized he was risking his life, his attention had been on the growing number of feed sacks filled with rocks containing gold. He had built this tunnel as fast as possible. The gold had been there for thousands of years, but he had needed to get at it immediately. Now he was paying the price for that greed, a price he might not live to afford. The same horizontal shaft that was to provide his fortune would prove to be his end.

He couldn't laugh at the humor in that. There was not enough air for him to take a deep breath, and certainly none left for the luxury of laughing. He vowed to laugh more often if he should get out of this predicament, which at the moment seemed impossible. He moved in and out of consciousness. Whenever the fear, the idea of pain or thoughts about his predicament became too great, he went to sleep, becoming unconscious. His mind remained active enough to dream of many things he had not done yet.

In his waking moments he made the best of a bad situation by imagining what he would do if he did get out, thinking of the wealth he had managed to scrape from the ground—enough, if there ever was such a thing. He pictured a wedding, himself the groom, but try as he might he could not see through the bride's veil. He had never considered getting married, had always assumed that a

wife and children would come some day, but when and where remained a mystery. Again came the temptation to laugh, lying eight feet underground, trapped for life, and imagining his own wedding. A brother was there, as were a father and mother. He looked happy enough, but so thin, the ceremony so serious. Was this a wedding that was to be? Was it a cruel joke? Or was it a gift to pass the time and tempt him to live?

He dreamed on. His son, walking along a deserted road. Sandy hair, medium build, and so intense. He walked with such vigor and strength that his walking seemed to move the road rather than the other way around. Of course he had no son. The dream seemed so real, however, that from then on he believed that there would some day be a son for him. The conviction of this very thought saved him from the fear of the predicament. He focused so intensely on the thought that he hardly noticed himself dissolving. Physicalness disappeared as the thought rose, out of the ground, his body materialized above ground not hurt at all.

There is nothing like our own mortality to tenderize us. People often act as though they will live forever, a concept that allows all kinds of callous and insensitive behaviors. Paul, right now, was savoring life.

He used most of his remaining water to boil three small potatoes. To his heightened senses, the potatoes smelled particularly intoxicating. An unusual calm spread over him as he ate. Forgetting his routine eating habits, he appreciated every mouthful of the meal. Each bite was special.

The sun was high in the sky by the time he broke camp and continued the climb. There was little variance in the terrain: rocks and more rocks, with blue sky overhead. It was a new day, he was in Colorado, and after all, dreams were just dreams. Although his mortality was close at hand, he was more alive than ever. His optimistic energy returned, chasing away the unusual calm he had experienced at breakfast.

The day grew hotter and the conversations in his head grew louder. They were always on the same subject—water. He had only been hiking for a little over a day and was already running out. A line he had come up with for an English class assignment echoed in his head: "If you plan a trip through the desert to avoid mirages, you won't miss anything." He had been quite proud when he wrote his poetically ambiguous line, but he had not been thirsty. He was not thirsty yet, but thirst was not nearly as far away as a water supply. The combination of the sun, dryness, and altitude were something he had not planned on. He was dehydrating and afraid to drink the little bit of water left in the old olive-green army canteen.

Only a darned fool goes hiking without enough water and without a map to water. The dry scratchiness

in the back of his throat reminded Paul he was a darned fool, a thirsty darned fool.

Water was something he had always taken for granted. Normally he drank more water than anyone he knew. Probably drank at least a gallon a day, which made this lack of water all the more unsettling.

He was so busy thinking about water that he failed to notice the clouds moving in from the west. The crash of thunder caught his attention just moments before he was drenched by a deluge. There he was, obsessing about the lack of water, and suddenly wet to the bone.

Running around like a lunatic, he laughed, cried, thanked God for the rain and laid out a piece of plastic, ran a trough down the middle and collected water in the canteen. He thought of people in the city who try and stay out of the rain, then remembered he used to be one of them. It rained for half an hour, enough time to fill his canteen, have a shower, and drink his thirst away.

Two days later, basking in the glow of his first campout, Paul returned to campus to the strains of Steppenwolf's "Magic Carpet Ride" played at maximum volume.

Paul had arrived just in time for registration and the celebration that accompanied it. The music was great, registration was necessary, and the beanies that were required attire for each freshman were entirely unnecessary. Paul found himself standing in the shortest lines around. Nobody but Paul, it seemed, was interested in ethics or meta-physics.

He had never been much of a student in high school, receiving mostly average grades while always thinking he was far above average. His only distinction in high school was the long hair he grew his sophomore year. That year there were only four people with long hair in a school of over three thousand students. He stuck out and received plenty of ridicule that he considered flattering attention.

He did not really need the attention, but did not turn it down either. By his junior year, when there were hundreds of kids with long hair, he had outgrown the need for it. His hair had seemed so important one year and had lost all of its significance the next. He had even run away from home because his father wanted him to cut his hair. His father hadn't seemed to care much about him until there was a problem. Paul's hair provided just such a problem, and a confrontation that seemed so significant at the time.

Now everyone, it seemed, was looking for significance—or trying to escape it. The 60's had arrived.

Paul had outgrown existentialism, didn't care to read more surrealist plays, and no longer had a dog to walk. He was in college now, and had moved on to reading Zen Buddhism wherever he was and during virtually any waking moment. As he read he remembered the moment of the shot on the mountain, and realized that it was an enlightening experience. Outside of thought. Like being hit on the head with a master's stick, the gun shot and concurrent surprise had awakened a part of him for the first time since early childhood. To get outside of thought, outside of self, beyond being—that was how he saw Zen. But he wanted it so badly that he kept it at bay.

Paul had been told that college was different from high school, with fewer rules and more respect. He believed it until he got reprimanded for reading Zen Buddhism in a botany lecture. Studying and not thinking are an odd combination, but Paul was young, energetic and naive enough to tackle both at the same time.

His first camp-out had taught him that his body was not really ready for the mountains, and that his mind was not, either. He started running Football Mountain, early, while the members of the football team were still asleep. And Zen seemed to fulfill the irony and paradox that he needed to take himself less seriously. "What is the sound of one hand clapping?" he thought whenever he got a chance. He wasn't sure, but knew that his teachers did not have the answer either.

Reading Zen also provided Paul with multiple perspectives. He could observe himself and the students around him with many different, and sometimes opposing, views. This was the 60's, a time when students took their causes very seriously. There was a group of students who were rebelling against "the system." What system there was at Western State Colorado Paul could not quite figure out. There did not seem to be anything cohesive enough in the small mountain town to be called a system.

"Well," he thought, "if there are to be protesters, there must be something to protest." Paul spoke with several of these would-be campus radicals and suggested that what their cause needed was a martyr. No one was taking them seriously but themselves, and that was not the way it was supposed to be.

He suggested they hold a rally during which one of their members would get shot, from a distance. This would attract all kinds of attention to their cause.

The plan fell through for two reasons: First, no-body wanted to be the martyr, even though Paul only sug-gested being shot in the arm—as in, "What your organiza-tion needs is a shot in the arm." The other problem was finding a trustworthy marksman. There were plenty of locals who would have been delighted to do the shooting, but who prided themselves on killing what they were aim-ing at. Paul had never been interested in organizations, and this young Students-for-a-Democratic-Society group illustrated why. Too much theory and too little applica-tion.

"How come there's so much seriousness at a time when lightness is in order?" Paul thought. Apparently the students were more interested in their thinking than they were in the consequences or results of their thinking, or even the obvious everyday realities around them. To Paul, these people were feeding on esoteric ideas, ideals, and philosophies, all of which are pretty lean pickings.

After one week of classes, Paul had stopped car-ing how his studies were going—his Zen was progressing well, as if Zen could get somewhere. He meditated. He enjoyed the idea of simplicity and joy in the simple things in life—or better yet, in nothing at all. Things might have turned out very differently if he had been in a monastery, but he wasn't. He was kept busy juggling the nothingness of Zen and the supposed somethingness of college.

Another weekend rolled around. "Which way should I go? Does it matter?" Paul got a map from a local

gas station, spun a bottle on it which directed him north-
ward. He invited Liz, a perky brunette member of the
Students-for-a-Democratic-Society to go camping with
him. Much to his surprise, she agreed.

"What trail will we be taking?" she asked with the
innocence of an earnest radical. Paul pointed north, indicating that the closest the campout would get to structure
was direction. Liz gave him an odd look and backed out
of the trip.

Paul went by himself. This time he went with two
canteens of water and enough food for four days, though
he was only planning to go for two. He hiked north all
day, proud of the shape he was in both mentally and physically, delighted to be by himself, and only slightly miffed
that Liz did not join him for the campout.

That night he got into trouble again. No poachers
and no thirst, but an opponent much more dangerous than
any of these.

Peacefully he went to bed and slept well until the
middle of the night when he awoke to screaming in his
ears, throbbing in his head, and pain shooting through his
whole body. He was sick to his stomach, burning with
fever. He was in the mountains and seeing things all around
him that were not supposed to be in the mountains—
people, buildings, dragons, pyramids, deserts. There were
monsters, bright yellow and red, chasing him.

He had to run, escape their screaming, their dripping fangs and their eyes honed in on him. Running, run-

ning as fast as possible. Stumbling, falling often, desperate to get away. One rational thought at this moment might have given him the perspective needed, but rationality was not within his grasp. It was too dark to see anything except the monsters, who glowed brighter the faster they ran, a kind of internal brightness that shed no light on his path. Insanity had struck.

No pain now. Only the screaming in his head, and the running. Paul had no idea how much running and how much falling went on. He was an object. With insanity comes a loss of identity. His panic and flight were an attempt to outrun his own sickness, a race he was bound to lose.

This was the Hong Kong flu, an invitation through pain and disorientation to insanity. A virus, tiny as it is, threatening existence. Humbling? Yes, but humble is good in a world with subtlety so small and so influential that his life meant nothing to it. The virus itself could only temporarily threaten Paul's health. But his response and resistance to the virus, the running and craziness, offered a genuine threat. He had not even heard of the Hong Kong

flu, but that didn't impede its ability to infect and direct him. At the time, it seemed that he had been poisoned from within. His Zen did not help, neither did his training on football mountain nor did anything he had done, owned or accomplished in his life. This little virus had a way of exposing the supposedly meaningful as nothing.

He ran and fell most of the night, finally flopping into an unconscious heap until morning. He awoke delirious. Nothing seemed right yet he didn't have enough clarity to know what was wrong.

Paul looked up and saw another hallucination. A kind old face looking at him. The face looked weathered, somehow familiar, deeply concerned. There was wisdom in the expression and yet Paul could not hold on to that wisdom himself. His mind was nowhere that he recognized and his body was wedged against a boulder, on the edge of a cliff. There was blood all over him and the boulder, which had obviously deterred him from running off the cliff. The fact that his head did not hurt only emphasized how sick he was. His right arm lay limp at his side. There was a large ball of blood under the skin below the elbow, indicating a break, but there was no pain. He was too sick, unattached, and disoriented to take any of this personally. It did not seem real. He observed his sick, hurt and broken body like it was a photograph of himself, familiar yet detached.

The curtain of unconsciousness fell again and lifted hours later to the inane meaningless sounds of Muzak. It had to be a dream, but he had never had a dream with Muzak in it before.

It was not a dream. An old rancher had found his body. That explained the face he had seen, but little else. The rancher had noticed a tangle of blood and bruises, picked him up and carried him to his old truck, and driven him to the hospital. By the time he awoke, his arm was in a cast and his head was bandaged. Paul still had the Hong Kong flu, but by now it had run most of its course.

It is both humbling and scary to pass out and find everything unfamiliar upon awakening. One moment he was camping under the stars and the next looking up at a sprinkler screwed into a hospital ceiling to protect him in case of fire. What would protect him from himself, from the subtleties that he could not yet observe? Trust had gone and taken optimism with it. He had jeopardized his life, needlessly, and could not remember doing so. Is insanity really only a virus away? On his first camp-out, he had tackled the river, lack of water, and poachers. On his second camp-out, he had wrestled within himself and apparently lost, badly. One boulder had saved him from a completely crushed body and skull.

"Is there anything I can count on?" Paul wondered.

A good question, but none of the usual answers would do any more. His world, the one made up by him, was falling apart so rapidly that he was awake and yet did not know who he was.

People define themselves by their consistencies, and Paul was consistently losing his. Perhaps this was an invitation to trust the variability in life rather than the consistency, something that he had never thought of before. It was the only thought that consoled him now. Attempting to piece together the events that had brought him here, he was unable to do so. The memories of what he had done were missing, and so were recollections of the beasts chasing him. It was a blur—somehow he had gotten from his campsite to where he needed to be, the hospital, but it was unsettling to have hurt himself so badly in the process.

It had been over a week since his parents had heard from him. How do you tell your parents that you have been wandering around all night long hurting yourself and that you are in the hospital due to the grace of an old rancher?

"How are your classes, sweetie?"

"Fine."

Paul was too tired to figure out how to tell them tactfully, so he just told them the facts as he knew them. He also told them he was OK, a strange term to describe his present condition. His mother was worried, his father indifferent, preoccupied. It had to be an odd phone call for them—they were expecting the same Paul who had called a week earlier and the same Paul who had grown up in their house. Politely they ignored the differences

and accepted the call from a stranger as though it was
from their son.

Suddenly, Paul knew the courage and flexibility it
takes to be a parent was too much for him. He would
need to mature greatly before having a child of his own.

It was not the broken arm or the pain in his head
that bothered him most. It was the realization that trust in
himself had disappeared. The power of doubt is much
greater than that of certainty. Doubt blew down his house
of straw. Foresight would have let him know that these
events were a preparation, an opening up, but he had lost
the future, along with trust. The present had always been
unmanageable, but now it had lost even its pretense of
manageability. One moment he could be strong and deci-
sive; the next a raving idiot, totally unaware, running
through the mountains like a madman. If you can't trust
yourself, who can you trust? If you can't trust what you
have always trusted there is a gap, a daunting gap before
you grab on to the next thing or idea to trust.

Paul had always picked his few close friends carefully. One friend had always remained by his side, until
this moment. Now the rancher, doctor, and nurses were
all more dependable than he was.

Self-sufficiency, self-confidence, and self-image
seemed like illusions at this moment, as his identity disappeared into a necessary sea of acceptance. He couldn't
struggle any more, there was no Paul left. At this mo-

ment, he was not someone he would have chosen for a friend, he was nonexistent—at least until a new definition of existence occurred, a bigger one that included more than his old one, perhaps everything.

A strange peacefulness washed over Paul, washing away what he had perceived himself to be. A new perception must have to be more real than anything he had constructed before. Without knowing it, he was experiencing the effects of his Zen readings. The peacefulness was elusive, yet he knew it was more important, lighter and more pleasurable than anything else he had ever experienced. His identity was invisible and still there was something left that was at peace. Perhaps more accurately, what there was left *was* peace.

Sunday evening Paul left the hospital under his own power, a strange power that he had never felt before— almost as if there were no "I" there to feel it. Though he didn't realize it, his education had begun.

Our most important lessons in life always come when we are ready, though we seldom welcome them with open arms and often don't know that we are prepared, that, in fact, we have spent every moment of life preparing for each NOW. The lessons do not wait for our permission.

Paul took a cab to campus, the only taxi in town. He waved off questions from eager classmates when he returned to the dormitory in a cast and many bandages.

Liz was the most curious of all, fascinated by having almost shared the experience with him. He told her "the facts" and that he was very glad she had not come along.

The peaceful sensation remained deep inside him and had an effect on whomever and whatever he gave his attention. He discovered that in his present undefined, totally peaceful state he became a good student. Sitting passively in class and perceiving the teachers and the studies through a haze of unreality, he learned. He quickly changed from an average student to above average. Disinterest seemed to be what he had been missing. He continued to read Zen as he recuperated for the next several weeks. He did not have the strength or the desire to go back for his sleeping bag and camping supplies. Nor did he have the ability to put his identity back together. Sometimes he thought of himself as a sleep walker, and other times he basked in his ability to float so effortlessly through life while a new, deeper part of him took charge of awareness.

Life had become kind of a dream world for Paul. Nothing seemed real. His arm healed, but his view of reality did not.

One day Paul decided to stretch his hazy horizons in a fairly safe way and followed a group of students to a local "3.2 bar." To his question, Steve and Mel, the only students he knew who were *from* Gunnison, responded together, "That's the alcohol percentage in the beer!" They looked at him like he was from another planet.

Paul felt that way, but he didn't mind. He had only been to a bar twice before; both times were for a fish fry with his parents. Even more detached now, he sat near the door and watched the show, observing socialization in process.

A cute little blonde was flirting unmercifully with the captain of the football team. The dance of male and female played itself out, thwarted male and thwarted female. The indirect route was the road most traveled here. The blonde wanted the guy, but she did not dare ask. There was so much being communicated between the people at the bar underneath the social small talk.

This was a game Paul had never gotten good at; this talking without saying anything meaningful, while getting your message across covertly and making sure not to become too susceptible in the process.

In his head, he aged the couple at the other end of the bar by ten years, then twenty years, then thirty years. The football player had put on weight and was no longer working out. He still spoke of his college football days, but not to his thin, anemic blond wife, whom he rarely spoke to at all unless there were strangers around. He spoke to their two children about sports, but neither of them listened. The blonde's mouth drawn over her tight jaw, she still attempted to look young and cute, although she was neither.

Paul realized he was being unnecessarily negative, even though it seemed that the scenario played out in his head was a probable future for these two. Neither of them knew it; that was clear.

There was a stale smell in the air, cigarettes and beer, but one lone streak of sunlight was shining in through the 4-inch square window in the door, calling his attention to the outside. He was not interested. He continued to watch the people at the bar. Paul could picture himself with the blonde for an evening. What he did not want was her future. As Paul left the bar he thought, "Do we really live so much of our lives never saying what we really want to say, living by default, wandering around in a delirious state dealing only with what does not scare us too much?"

He read Zen as he walked home. Once inside his dorm room, he wound up, like a major league pitcher, and launched the Zen book as hard as he could against the far wall.

It hit with an unimpressive slap and fell to the floor, limp and lifeless. Zen was over for Paul. It was a waste of time and had nothing to offer him.

Five minutes later, Paul pulled the curtain closed and turned on the water in the community shower, shared by all the residents in the dormitory. As hot water cascaded over his head and down his back, the young blond girl cautiously entered the shower stall. She explained that she had followed him home from the bar. She wanted to make love with him, now. She reached out to him, and in her hand was the Zen book he had thrown away minutes before.

In that moment Paul woke up for the first time in his life. He stared at the shower curtain. He took nothing for granted. He found that the subtlest thing was of deep and profound interest. The blonde, of course, was not really there. But he was. Awake, alive and aware, more present than he had ever been before.

Awakening. Both subtle and blatant, it made everything other than this awakening seem hollow and empty. One moment of being awake is worth a lifetime of sleep.

Paul would always remember those moments in the dormitory shower stall. The soap. The curtain. The feeling of the water. To stand for one moment outside of the everyday illusion called reality—to see without a perspective and to be all of life—that is a first awakening. The new Paul stepped out of the shower and into a new life.

He was surprised to discover that up to this point, he had spent his life asleep, and unaware that he was asleep. The moment he declared that Zen had nothing to offer him, it gave him everything. What seemed impossible was revealed as the very stuff that life is made of. Life is nothing if not a conglomeration of the impossible, with a little bit of irony and a lot of paradox thrown in to spice things up. From one point of view life has to be serious, from two it can be interesting, from several perspectives it becomes humorous, and from many it becomes wise.

Inside the shower stall, the point of perspective from which Paul had viewed his entire life turned into several perspectives, and he laughed, freely, at nothing for the first time in his life.

Only as an infant could he have felt the same uncritical joy. The roughness of the towel as he dried himself was intense. The walk outside was so pleasant it seemed unbearable. It was. It didn't need to be borne, it could simply be experienced. When one is awake, everything is equally joyful and ecstatic. Everything is prayer and celebration. This or That disappears, and everything reveals itself in anything. Seeing, hearing and feeling become inclusive rather than exclusive. Paul included everything, and nothing. Perfection performed for him. It always had, but the show had never been available to him before.

Paul thanked Zen, and everything, at the same moment.

After his Zen awakening, Paul no longer *needed* to go camping. But that didn't stop him heading north the following weekend to retrieve his sleeping bag and camping supplies. He was surprised to discover his sleeping bag was occupied.

Paul was growing, changing, flowing between perspectives so rapidly that he had not even considered what condition he would find his sleeping bag in when he finally returned to the mountains.

Surprises were everywhere around him, so he took it in stride when he found the old rancher sleeping soundly in the summer sleeping bag. Patiently, he sat on a boulder and waited for the rancher to wake up. Two hours later, the old man was still snoring away. Paul got up stiffly and gave the rancher a polite shake.

He woke, blinked his eyes and said, "Just wanted to give you an opportunity to thank me proper for saving your life. Would have come to the hospital, but those places give me the creeps—too many sick people there for my liking."

Paul thanked him for his help. Before he could say more, the rancher crawled out of the sleeping bag, boots and all, and vigorously shook off rock dust. He looked like he had been crawling around in caves for weeks. Without stretching, or apologizing for getting the sleeping bag dirty, he headed down the mountain.

The old man moved faster than seemed possible, disappearing ahead of Paul to become but a momentary speck in the distance. How long the rancher had occupied the sleeping bag was hard to tell. The whole scene was so odd it was easier to forget he had even been there than to maintain the reality that he had. He was gone now; that was easier to handle.

As Paul turned the sleeping bag inside out to shake it, something metallic slid out, along with rock dust and dirt. The sound it made as it hit a rock gave away both its composition and location. Searching the ground, Paul discovered a shiny silver key. It was intricate beyond what seemed possible for its size. Its design was sweeping curves of filigreed metal, pleasing to look at, even better to trace his fingers along the curves as he imagined the fancy lock

the key would open. This was an old key, a work of art. It was doubtful that its beauty could have been duplicated by a craftsman of today. Whoever made this key was interested in the key for its own qualities and not just as a means to open a lock. It was a masterwork, an ornate piece of beauty resting in his hand. Was it an accident that the key was in his hand?

There was no chance of catching up with the rancher to return it to him. Paul slid it into his pocket after admiring it for a few more moments. He rolled up the sleeping bag and foam pad and scattered what little food the rancher had left behind for the birds and mice.

Slowly walking back toward campus with his camping gear, a very special key and no desire to camp ever again, he recalled his delirious night running through these mountains. By daylight they were bland and interesting, but not the least bit threatening. Rounding a large boulder, Paul came up short in front of what looked like the mouth of a cave. Moving closer to explore it, he discovered a shaft just big enough to crawl into, something he had no inclination to do.

The place seemed strangely familiar. The part of the shaft that could be seen was mostly horizontal, about eight feet clearly visible and another four or five fading into darkness. Just at the point were the darkness began, there was an object. Not big, but distinctly out of place.

Paul had experienced enough adventure lately, but his resistance was still low. He quickly succumbed to the temptation. Crawling into the shaft, and into the most obvious deja vu of his life, he discovered an old boot a few feet before a pile of loose rocks that almost entirely blocked the shaft. The boot was partly chewed by mice. It was old, cracked, and worn. The boot had lain in this shaft for many years.

Backing out with it, Paul examined it in the sunlight. It was the right boot and he was not the evil stepsister, but not yet convinced that he was Cinderella, either. Slipping off his own boot, Paul tried what remained of this one. It was a perfect fit. The unusual was becoming everyday to Paul. He replaced his much newer boot, crawled back down the shaft and put the old boot where it had been. As usual, there were too many explanations for his finding the cave and the boot, and the boot fitting him. His feet were size 12 1/2 medium, not a common size. None of the possible explanations were convincing, so he left them there at the mouth of the shaft and walked back to campus, mourning his loss of interest in camping.

Motivation had disappeared for Paul. He had depended on camping as a pastime that defined him. Now it was gone, and he had no idea what to do. He was not physically lost, but he did not recognize his mental surroundings. Camping, as a habit, remained.

Realizing that his college years were going to be more memorable than predictable—too many odd events

to make sense of—Paul stopped trying to figure things out.

He had moments of inclusion, resisting nothing and embracing everything without distinction. In these moments all contrast was lost. It was in one of these presently neutral moods that Paul returned from the mountains. Until he got to his dorm room and found his roommate home.

As a child, Paul had been told it was bad to be judgmental. "Be nice to your cousins." And, "Don't fight." Later this turned into a general judgment against judging other people. This internal contradiction was too much for Paul. Obviously everybody was judging everything all the time, just not talking about their judgments. Judgment is the way the mind works. It was the way he had decided to go to college in Colorado—without it any college would have been the same. Without judgment, and his identity to hold it, he surely would not have been here NOW.

Judgment was exclusion. Anything but NOW was falling out of the inclusionary state of awareness. It was from a state of inclusion that Paul had been able to remain at a distance from his roommate—as far as possible. The two young men were different, and not the least bit complementary. Paul had never consumed alcoholic beverages, and his roommate Jeff, had seldom spent a sober night since high school. What greeted Paul as he walked into the room was Jeff's drunken snores and the stink of urine.

This was the third—and, he decided, the last—time Paul would clean up the late urine puddle in the middle of the dorm room floor as Jeff slept off his stupor. Gritting his teeth Paul *judged* that it was time to get rid of his roommate.

From that night on, he slept with the windows wide open, giving his roommate a literally cool reception. The next time Jeff staggered home past midnight, drunk but not so anesthetized he didn't feel the cold, he realized he was not welcome. He left for a friend's dorm room. The scenario repeated twice before Jeff started moving his things across campus.

The idea concerning judgments, Paul had discovered, was not to avoid them but merely to hold them loosely. Holding to a judgment results in stagnation; not making a judgment results in no learning; making and then releasing a judgment results in growth. Paul had just reaped the rewards.

Rewards, though, would not prove that predictable. Returning from class to his now private dorm room Paul found a visitor waiting for him. Liz, his almost camping companion, was clutching her books in agitation. There was to be a rally of the Students-for-a-Democratic-Society that very evening, and the scheduled speaker had just canceled. Paul's earlier advice to the group had impressed them—at least enough to choose him over no speaker.

During the three seconds it took to decline the offer in no uncertain terms, Paul relived his public speaking debut in high school speech class. His four-minute prepared speech about the existence of God had been delivered in 30 seconds flat, leaving Paul the indelible memory of standing in front of a room full of people for 3 1/2 minutes of mind-bending, soul-torturing silence.

Liz gnawed her lip, disappointed.

Paul took a deep breath, "How about if I find a replacement speaker?" Liz beamed as she eagerly accepted.

Paul telephoned his ethics professor, who was flattered by the invitation and accepted. Paul figured if anything could settle down a radical group, it was his ethics professor. He was the only one who considered himself radical—his lectures were slow, measured, and barely endurable.

That evening Paul and Liz headed off to the rally arm in arm. Liz, bouncing with eagerness and quoting Marx, tugged Paul along. She never seemed to realize that the radical rally had been turned into another boring college lecture. There were plenty of references to philosophers from Kant to Shopenhaur, but no call to action. Most philosophers, it seemed, favored intellectualizing over action. But Liz enjoyed the lecture—there is nothing like philosophy to spark a Home Economics major.

Having saved the day, Paul invited Liz to go camping with him the following weekend.

With a smile, she patted him on the shoulder. "Sorry, I've already made plans!" So much for rewards.

Paul didn't see Liz again until Friday afternoon as he descended the dormitory steps wearing his backpack. Liz was out in front of the dorm, waiting in line to board a bus taking a group of coeds on an organized camping trip to the Arapaho Forest Camp Grounds. Jeff, Paul's newly departed roommate, was standing behind her, clearly mustering his forces to score.

Paul wasn't sure how attracted to Liz he was but seeing her beside Jeff seemed to settle it. He shook his head and began his hike.

As Paul walked west he thought about his father. Of all the times they had not shared together, and how he had always needed to act badly to get attention. His most recent episode at the hospital had left his father with hospital bills and insufficient explanation of what had happened. This had resulted in several letters and, he suspected, numerous calls he had not answered. Paul was a different person now, in a new world, and he had no interest in keeping up the old routines with his father. At some point he would answer a letter or call, but he was in no hurry. Perhaps someday he would appreciate his father, but until then close contact seemed impossible. Paul and his father had always been distant. Maybe it was appropriate that by attending Western State Colorado Paul was putting real miles between them.

West: that was the direction this weekend—alone. A very different camper headed west from the one who had hiked southeast upon his arrival in Gunnison. Paul had been seasoned, humbled, broken, scared, and awakened. He no longer bothered to look in the mirror because the person who looked back was unrecognizable. Twenty pounds and many illusions lighter, he was lean and muscular. His thoughts were lean, too. The conversations in his head were still there, but quieter than ever before. With this quiet came respect and peacefulness. He was closer to empty and closer to happy than he had ever been before.

Paul walked for hours, enjoying the rough mountains and wide open skies but not dwelling on them. He was alone and enjoying his own company. Occasionally a thought of Liz and Jeff surfaced. Life seemed so simple for them, but he would not have traded places with them for anything. Perhaps Liz and Jeff belonged together, perhaps not. It did not seem to matter, though Paul still thought about them.

He made camp early that evening, then watched the sun set. After building a fire with what little wood he could find, he sat watching the flames, not really thinking, not really aware. Just Paul and the mountains. And— "What?"

He heard a Voice. The Voice was different from any he had ever heard—it spoke strongly and yet peacefully and quietly. It was not within him, he heard it through his ears but it entered him and filled him. All of his awareness was instantly heightened and focused on that Voice.

McBroom, goes the tall tale, had a one-acre farm. His soil was so fertile that when he planted his first row of beans, the stalks blossomed and were ready for picking before he finished the row. The topsoil was so rich that seeds just sprang to life. But he found out that planting corn could be dangerous. If he did not move fast enough, the stalk would shoot up and scrape the skin off his nose. Paul may not have been as fertile as McBroom's topsoil, but all the events of his life had led him to this point of readiness.

"Welcome," said the Voice.

It was a loud whisper, neither male or female. Paul looked around and held up his lantern, but there was nobody to see. It had to be the old rancher. Paul stood up and searched. The rancher was not there, so obviously he must be hearing things.

Again the Voice spoke. "Welcome. I have been waiting for you."

Doubting his own sanity, Paul wondered if talking to nobody was really that much crazier than talking to somebody. Often enough, he had talked to people who were apparently not listening or did not seem to understand or care about what he was saying. Maybe it made more sense to talk to nobody. This nobody with a Voice just might be able to hear exactly what he said.

"Hi there," he said, assuming the possessor of the Voice could only hear what was said out loud, an assumption he made with other people everyday. He would learn later that people, and particularly this entity, could listen into thoughts, all thoughts, even his most private ideas. Everything about him was in the public domain. But he didn't know that yet.

The Voice did not reply. After a few seconds of listening, the conversations in Paul's head resumed. Was there really a Voice, or just an imaginary one?

He would find out later that the Voice is always there, everywhere, waiting to converse and in the process of conversing. It lacks nothing but a listener, in this case Paul. The Voice is so polite that as long as a person is speaking out loud or in his or her own head, it will not interrupt. The Voice requires no animate object to speak through. All that seems so real to us is just an expression

of the Voice, an interpretation of the Voice in a specific location. When an avenue is open, and the animal or person is ready, perfection manifests itself as the Voice speaks. It waits, patiently, for the kind of silence that sometimes results from emergencies or meditation.

During an emergency, the Voice is heard but not recognized, and it will often say something that would be entirely misinterpreted in an ordinary moment. It might say something like, "Pick up the car." The person reaches down and picks up a real car to save someone lying underneath it. It also might say, "Look behind the third oak on the left, three miles down County Trunk M. That is where the body is buried." The Voice hummed, and Beethoven wrote a symphony. It whispered and the four minute mile was broken, a perfect gymnastic routine performed. It uttered a few words, and George Bernard Shaw wrote another play. All that is good in us is a result of the interpretation of the Voice. There is only one Voice.

The Voice generates perfection in every utterance. It directs an obedient universe like a good dog trainer directs a dog to lie down or sit up and beg. Most of the time human beings are too noisy to hear the Voice, and the result is the jumbled consequence we call life.

In this moment Paul was ready, or he would not have heard the Voice. Everything in his life had prepared him for this moment, and from his perspective it was not clear whether the Voice spoke to him because of his problems or as a reward for growing up sufficiently over the last several weeks. He heard the Voice, and then missed the opportunity to hear it again by talking to himself about the Voice. One utterance from the Voice is often sufficient to inspire a whole novel, but in this case it incited only a riot of questions and poorly constructed answers.

He waited with his loud version of patience for the Voice to speak again. There are people who hear the Voice once and never again. They wait in vain their whole lives for the perfection they glimpsed in that moment. The Voice appears as visions to some people and revelations to others. There are people who take drugs to hear the Voice, others who sit in caves, and still others who walk on red hot coals or climb mountains. None of these activities makes hearing the Voice more likely. All it needs is nothing, and all a person needs to hear it is a moment of silence. Perhaps Paul's chance had passed.

He had been taught that people who hear Voices are crazy. That lie believed stops most people from conversing with the universe knowingly. So Paul was crazy. A crazy young man, sitting and waiting.

Hours passed. Finally sleep overtook him. The last thing he remembered before nodding off was hearing the Voice again—he thought. The bridge between waking and sleeping sometimes provides a brief access to the Voice. In the busyness of so many people's lives, this transition is the only opening they have.

"Learn to quiet down. The moment you are quiet, you will hear me."

Paul only vaguely heard this at the time, but remembered it vividly as he awoke with the sun the next
day. He was warm and comfortable in his winter sleeping
bag, engaging in a conversation in his head about how to
quiet the conversations in his head. Counter-productive,
at best. Paul thought the conversations in his head were
who he was. Those very conversations blocked perfection from manifesting within him.

He breathed deeply of the heavy morning air and
heard the Voice say, "Look." He looked. He saw the
mountains, the sleeping bag, and the sky. The sun, which
was only partially above the horizon, suddenly dipped back
down, peeked up and then back down again like a child
playing hide and seek.

*It didn't matter how many masts of ships Colum-
bus had seen as they arrived in port. They were always
shorter in appearance the further they were away. The
idea of a round Earth was not held by enough people to
be believed by any. Columbus had to hold the idea himself, had to nurture it and feed it while being willing to
risk his life to discover for himself that it was true. No
amount of money, no degree of public recognition or
power, could drive a person to live so intimately and alone
with an idea. Only conviction.*

*With evidence, the idea of the roundness of Earth
became a fact. Nobody needed to believe it anymore.*

Paul had just joined Chris in the holding of the impossible. The sun rises in the east and sets in the west. Be damned the present reality that it neither rises nor sets at all. We still say it does and are egocentric enough that we can observe a sunrise when there isn't any.

Now, here was the evidence for him. The proof of the insecurity and obscurity of so-called facts had arrived. This was not a hallucination, and there were no drugs involved. This had happened. Of the people who saw it, some laughed to see such a joke, some cried, and most just didn't believe their eyes.

Paul was awestruck. Did the whole Earth move, or just the horizon? Could the sun have made the movements? He recalled a saying his grandfather used when faced with something particularly confusing or upsetting. He would say, "At least the sun still rises in the east and sets in the west." His grandfather was dead and gone, and so was counting on the sun to do what he said it would.

Though Paul had lost the ability to trust himself, he had gained the willingness to trust nature. The sun was part of nature. Initially, he was surprised by its behavior. This surprise led to laughter and his second large dose of awakening. In that moment, he had interrupted the conversations in his head long enough to hear the Voice say, "Good. That's it. You are welcome."

What do you do when your whole world, or perhaps the sun, has been turned upside down? It was a revelation and a miracle. So far, only from Paul's perspective.

He would not tell anyone else about what had happened. You just cannot tell people that the sun winked at you. You can tell people all kinds of ordinary things, but extraordinary experiences are personal. Communication is reserved for the meaningless mundane aspects of everyday life. People throughout the ages have gotten themselves into deep trouble by trying to communicate messages of intense value.

Paul packed up camp, keeping some attention on the sun, hoping to witness another trick.

He had learned that morning that nothing is ordinary. We miss the obvious delight of everything by focusing on what we call extraordinary. We notice a flat tire immediately, but fully inflated tires elude our perception. We lose the ability to derive delight from the ordinary and attend more to problems, the extraordinary. This approach allows us to miss so much—almost everything. It also encourages us to travel to distant places to find what is right within us all the time.

This morning nothing was to be taken for granted. Paul kept an eye on the sun and also attended to everything else. Who knows where or when the next miracle will occur? He began to realize that perhaps miracles are happening all the time, but people are too busy to notice them. And busyness is not the only obstruction to seeing miracles; compulsion to make life predictable made people miss miracles happening each moment right before their eyes.

Paul continued his hike, heading uphill and getting into a rhythm. People say, "Give me a sign, then I will know, then I will believe." The effect this sign had on Paul was to awaken him. The appropriate response to seeing such a sign is a genuine Thank-you, and getting on with life.

Around midday he reached a series of cliffs. Though he liked to hike, he had never done any serious mountain climbing. These cliffs were too steep for him to climb, so he skirted them looking for a place to gain more altitude safely. Walking his way around them, he discovered a narrow path that led steeply upward. He followed it to the top of the first cliff. The view from the top was breathtaking—the mountains, sky and sun dancing together to create a light and shadow show. The breathtaking view was a miracle in itself.

Paul felt a twinge in his abdomen, the kind of feeling you get at the top of a roller coaster, just before going down, the moment of pause between the peak and tearing down the trough.

It was then that he heard the Voice again. It said, "Fall forward. Things won't always be this easy."

One moment it was business as usual. He crawled, he ate, and he slept. His world was a small place, the undersides of leaves and their tops. In the morning the leaves were usually wet, and by midmorning they were often dry. He preferred the dry, but could eat either. The leaves themselves provided him with all the water he needed, and everything else as well. Each new leaf was a new world, an un-holy world that needed holes in it, and he needed the nourishment that the holes would give him. He was trapped, but unlike the miner he didn't know it.

It is easier to escape when you have sufficient perspective to know you are caught. He could not remain the way he had always been, and survive, so he had to transform. He cut himself off from food and embraced one of the magical changes in nature.

He fastened his old self permanently to a substantially holy leaf. Fastened himself so well that he would have to do something radical or die. He did this early in the morning, and spent the day without food or drink. It was a long day. It took many hours to change his mind sufficiently so that his body could follow during the night. At dawn, the next day, the magical process began.

He began spinning. He had never even heard of spinning before, and now he was consumed by it. He bound himself like a mummy, wound himself around and around, tied himself so thoroughly that the outside world vanished and the only world there was existed inside this cocoon. Once that was done he rested.

There was nothing to do in such a tight space. What came next did not seem like work at all. He began to rearrange and change himself. Chemicals swished and swirled. Arms formed where there had been none. He created and destroyed. He became God within his own limitations.

What had appeared to be soft but solid became liquid, lost form, and then had the option of taking a new form again. He had no idea what he was building, but had all of the abilities to go on with the work of art. If we have to know in advance what it is we do, so little is possible for us, and certainly nothing so daring as the transformation that was happening here.

Within two weeks, which seemed like forever, he was hungry. The hunger was not like it had been before, not even in the same place, but he didn't know that. He had no memory of the past. In this change he had moved on irretrievably, outgrown what he'd been, and transformed. Now he needed food. He ate, and as he ate became aware of light, not in the way we see it but from head to toe sensing the light and knowing it was good. He emerged from what had seemed a death trap and had actually been a chamber of impossible opportunity. He was an alchemist converting the impossible to the possible.

He crawled out, spread his wings—WINGS!—and flew to a honeysuckle flower, knowing deep within him what to do. He reached in and received the sweet reward for his labors. The old leaves could not compare with the heady, intense energy he got from that flower, but he didn't remember the leaves. He flew from flower to flower that day, strengthening himself until he could be the inspiration, with a friend, for another generation of the marvelous change of life.

If he had known, tied to the leaves, what he knew now, his life would have been miserable. But he was a creature of the moment. Replenished, he flew for the fun of flying. He flew into the proximity of the future mother of his children, and she, new to the world also, flew to him. Together, their wings explored the same air for the first time.

"What does a caterpillar think of in the cocoon?"

Probably nothing, was his answer as he phased in and out of sleep, trapped as the caterpillar had been. Earlier that morning, he could crawl in and out of the shaft with the gold that his labors produced. Now, pinned by the rockfall, he could not. Some kind of a transformation must ensue.

He did not have to build his cocoon because the mine had already provided that. From the moment he had found the gold, he had been like a man possessed, like a caterpillar interested in nothing but gold leaf. The only way he could get out of the mine and stay out was to cycle from his life as a miner, and then be resurrected. His body would not change like the caterpillars, except for the brief moment in which he escaped. His mind had to change in ways that were entirely inconceivable to him and almost everyone else. He had to totally forget the man he had been, and disappear. He then had to rebuild a new identity from nothing, or not have an identity. Accordingly, all that he had called himself started to fade away.

From the perspective of the Voice, these changes were everyday events. As obvious as night and day. As natural as the movement of caterpillar to butterfly, of bodies to dust and back to bodies again.

So his mind transformed. All he had thought, the

narrow viewpoint he had on life, the greed and the short-sightedness, disappeared along with his youth. The miner disappeared, and a rancher was born.

A rancher in the most expansive sense of the word. A rancher of nature. A person interested in open spaces and anything that could live there—the more space the better. Tight spaces were no longer for him. He had grown beyond them.

Suddenly, blinking in the sun, the former miner was sitting outside of the shaft. Feeling his new muscles, he stretched and yawned, oblivious to the magic that had just happened, surprised to find bags of gold around himself. It could have been amnesia, had there been an observer, but he didn't even remember that he didn't remember.

He would use the gold to purchase as much land as possible. He would leave digging to others. He would have wild horses on his land, and cattle. He would cherish the open sky and rejoice in his freedom. Spread his wings. He would marry, and within nine months have a daughter.

In the transition he had lost his personality and one boot. He walked, one shoe on and one shoe off, into Gunnison. The escape had been nothing special to the mind. Just impossible. To the miner the cave-in had meant death, so the miner had died. He had changed so thoroughly into a rancher that the rocks could no longer hold him. It was a rancher who purchased a horse and cart.

He carted the gold to town and was greeted with open arms by the bank president, a depositor with more in his cart than the total assets of the bank. The old vault was no longer sufficient. A row of ornate, decorative vaults was created for special depositors. A new era was born, and with it Gunnison grew.

Much of the gold went for the purchase of land, but from that point on the rancher never ran low on money. Sufficiency is a state of mind, as is luxury, and the miner had lacked both. The rancher did not.

"Fall forward."

The Voice seemed to be speaking only to Paul. It was not. At that same moment it was speaking to everyone, and there were some people able to hear it. Some fell forward, and some did not.

A camel driver in the Sudan was sitting on his camel, thirsty and poised over what he thought was a mirage. He fell forward—into a pool of warm but satisfying water. A door-to-door salesman had just had the door slammed in his face for the twenty-third time that day. He did not fall forward—but walked to the next house. A diver in Moscow was performing her final competitive dive before retiring at the tender age of twenty-eight. She heard the Voice and trusted it. She fell forward—into the best dive of her life, a perfect 10.

For each person the Voice presented a possibility of trust and perfection. An offer, if accepted, that provided a connection with the universe far beyond individual expression.

In each moment trust is available. Some people hear the Voice, most do not. The Voice is always speaking, and whether people hear it or not, they are influenced by it. All thoughts and behaviors are the result of this influence. Listening, trusting, and surrendering to the Voice leads to perfection and the realization of that perfection. Not hearing it leads to perfection but not the realization of it. What made the dive perfect was the Voice. What would have made it imperfect is a matter of human standards and rules. The Voice expresses in the dive, but only when we hear it does the perfect appear to us.

Paul did not fall forward. In that moment, when trust was so necessary, he did not trust. After all, this was a new Voice, to him, and a very old cliff.

In his life he had had numerous opportunities to trust, and always avoided those times like the plague. It is at these moments that we are tested, and who we really are appears through the mist of who we think we are. Moments of trust can be as simple as falling backwards into someone's arms, jumping off a diving board, or letting yourself flow freely in white water rapids. Every time it gets dark, people have to go to sleep, turn on a light, or

trust themselves. No matter how many times we receive the opportunity to trust, we do not accept it often. Those all-too-numerous trusting opportunities declined had led to this big moment for Paul.

He rolled to the side instead of falling forward.

The next moment there was a cracking sound, a sucking noise as his chest broke open right down the middle. There was a fluttering sensation, followed by a sharp pain. His heart fell out of his chest and slid to the ground.

His heart—still beating and attached to him—lay on the rock, pulsating.

He screamed out in anguish. There was no more pain, only fear. He was terrified. He had heard that at moments like this, life flashes before one's eyes. Nothing that exotic or exciting happened. He just looked at his heart. If it had eyes, it would have looked back at him.

He cautiously sat up, cradling his heart in his trembling hands, sliding it back into his chest. There was still no pain. The opening in his chest closed as quickly as it had opened. There was not even a scar. It took Paul several minutes to recover even slightly from that experience. His breath caught in his throat, and he had to cough, almost gagging to break the state of shock. Deep sadness wavered through him and quickly disappeared.

Before he had regained enough strength to stand, he angrily screamed, "You call that easy?!"

He was answered by the simple word, "Yes."

Standing with clenched fists, he puffed himself up, self-righteous, ready to berate the Voice. He paused, remembered who he was talking to, and said nothing.

The Voice said, "Life is easier when consequences are obvious."

Having his heart fall out was not a consequence he had ever expected, but it was one to learn from. The Voice had told him specifically what to do, and he had done something else. He vowed to do what the Voice said from then on.

Each day we make so many little compromises that erode trust, eating away at our strength as human beings. We sweep dust under the rug and pretend it isn't there. We say we will do something and then don't. We live as if what we do and say don't matter. Then we wonder why we don't trust ourselves. We ignore the second rule of the universe—the universe never forgets. The first rule is that there are no accidents. The universe never sleeps and it never forgets. We sleep and forget, and the more we have to forget, the more we sleep.

Paul sat, meditating, for the rest of the day. Waiting for the Voice to say, "Lean forward," again. He was ready now. Scared, but knowing he would lean forward in an instant now. He even practiced leaning forward as far as he could without falling, physically taunting the Voice to tell him to lean forward again. His own internal voices

and the distant cry of a hawk as it circled overhead were all he heard.

He sat, waiting. Dusk came, and went. It had been easier to sit at the edge of the cliff during the day. The darkness brought with it fear and invisibility. There was no moon this night so Paul could not even see the cliff. He continued to lean too far forward for comfort. As dawn approached, he leaned even further, tempting fate.

The Voice spoke again: "Lean back."

He leaned back, all the way back to a lying position, and fell asleep.

It was past midday when Paul awoke. The cliff was still there. He was still there. He rubbed his chest to verify that it was still there. The events of the previous day and night seemed like a dream, but he knew they were real. His body ached, and he shivered from deep within with cold and stiffness. Carefully, he stood up and stretched. It took several minutes to regain comfortable use of his arms and legs. Certainly, he had stayed up all night before, but never on the edge of a cliff waiting for an unknown Voice to prompt him to fall.

He was calm and peaceful, more peaceful than he had ever been before. He fixed himself breakfast. Eating it slowly, Paul attended to each bite with the care of a condemned man at his last meal. He ate the trail mix one piece at a time, experiencing the sweetness of each raisin, the abundant flavors of the nuts and seeds. Never had water tasted so good before. He didn't want to miss a thing. There was something exquisite in each subtle movement, in the slightest touch or taste. He hoped he would never forget. The universe was his, but he did not want it. Life was his, but he did not own it. He was experiencing something more precious: a moment of being...without conversation...nothing to do...no past...no future.

The Voice, too polite to interrupt an ongoing conversation, was not likely to interrupt the bliss he was experiencing. The first few experiences of bliss are seldom recognized until they are gone. It takes practice to notice bliss while you are experiencing it.

The world was Paul's university, experience his teacher, and he was learning. It was not his long night on the cliff, or even his heart falling out, that had led to his current state of bliss. If you have to sit on a cliff, or travel to India, or lose, however temporarily, an internal organ to attain this state, then it is not really bliss.

Paul smiled. It seemed that his smile consumed his whole face, his body, the mountain and perhaps the universe. He remembered the Cheshire cat that faded away leaving only its smile. He thought about meeting that cat and exchanging smiles.

The sun paused at its apex then headed to the second half of the horizon. A breeze arose, telling Paul it was time. He headed toward Gunnison, a combination of walking and floating. Never had he covered so much

ground so easily. Aware of his body more than ever before, he was observing its movements rather than experiencing them. Like a cat he moved, effortlessly and with complete awareness. Up until today, his body had been a vehicle to move his mind around. Now he was floating, arms and legs moving freely, unencumbered by his mind. He had become larger than his thoughts and thus could observe them without being them. Geographically and physically, he was above his thinking. Laughter welled up inside him and escaped, lightening and lighting him up further.

He arrived, blissfully, at his dorm room door. A surprise was there. Another visitor.

He had just delighted in the most rewarding and freeing experience of his life, experiencing bliss like nothing he imagined possible, and now here was his father. They moved toward each other. Paul's arms were outstretched to hug his father and he did not notice until too late that his father's right arm was coiled, ready to strike.

A closed fist met his cheek, driving him backwards and to the floor, where he slumped unconscious.

The next thing Paul saw was his father standing in the middle of the dorm room, relieved and quite proud of himself for having hit his son so hard. He had just released years of repressed anger. The huge hospital bill and unreturned calls had been the final straw in an anger that had been building in his father for years. Though the blow had been directed toward Paul, the anger was not nearly so personal. His father was not especially angry at him.

Lack of self expression can only last so long until it erupts unharnessed. Oddly enough, this was an opportunity for the closeness Paul and his father had never found.

Moments before, Paul had been floating, ultimately happy; now he was lying on the floor, leaning against the closet door, ears ringing in pain. The whole side of his head throbbed from the blow.

Paul's recent experiences had given him the flexibility of numerous perspectives, not just reaction. One moment he wanted to hit his father back. Next he pondered the use of a crack on the head in Zen. His father became a Zen master, teaching Paul wisdom.

Paul stood and embraced his father. Held him close and felt the love that resides, often hidden, in every family relationship. Warmth tingled from head to toe. He laughed inside, smiled outside, and kept on hugging. "Dad."

Paul's father was a musician—a lover, not a fighter. He was an only child whose deepest emotions up to this point were expressed in oboe solos. He spoke through his instrument, not in words. He had been silent while Paul was growing up, but now the flood gates had opened.

In human beings there is a prolonged dependence between parent and child. The dependence for food and shelter lasts for years. The emotional dependence, based

on insecurity and beliefs, usually lasts a lifetime. Typically there are enough incompletions and unexpressed emotions to color all later interactions and keep therapists couches full.

No other species has the kind of extended dependence our children have with their parents. This relationship is often explored for a lifetime. Unlike people, dogs seldom even know their fathers, and only depend on their mothers while they are puppies. They never get together for holidays or expect emotional support.

Imagine a water spaniel pondering his emotional instability and attributing it to not knowing his father! Mating is the closest a male dog gets to parenting. The male dog has one chance to influence its offspring—through genes. The human being has both genetics and learning to influence its offspring. The dog cannot be taught to sit by its mother, but the human being is taught not only how to sit, but when, where, and with whom. People model behaviors for their children for many years, ensuring that some good and some bad traits are passed on to another generation. Paul had not inherited his father's musical ability, but he had learned his way to use silence to end an argument.

Neither Paul or his father knew what their relationship could be, but for the first time there was an opening to find out.

Paul looked at his father and said, "What the heck did you hit me for?"

"Because you were ready for it," his dad replied. "I have waited my whole life to do that to someone, and I don't even know why. I just needed to."

His head still hurt, but Paul was more curious than angry. Curious about his relationship with his father, what it had been, what it could be. Wondering what it would be like to have his father as a friend, a confidant. He had expected things from his father that could not be politely asked of a friend. His father had seldom lived up to these expectations, and Paul had always condemned his dad's shortcomings. Now he realized that the problem was in his expectations.

His father was acting spontaneously now, and that alone blew apart Paul's expectations. The visit, and the punch to Paul's head, amounted to two spontaneous acts in one day. He had bought the plane ticket only that morning. He hadn't discovered the real reason for coming until he hit Paul. He'd thought he was coming to resolve the hospital bill.

He looked at Paul and grinned. "Let's talk son."

Paul beamed back, still somehow floating in the lightness the Voice had left him.

His father's reservation on a return flight was for the next morning, so they had little time to enjoy their new friendship.

Paul had heard a story of an old man who had become senile. After ten years of senility, he was walking

out of his room into the hallway of his home and bumped into his wife. In the moment of the collision he regained his rationality. Husband and wife spent the next two hours at the kitchen table in nonstop conversation. They spoke of old times, caught up on what he had missed, and talked about the future. At the end of two hours, the man gradually faded back into his senile trance.

The visit from Paul's father was much like that couples time at the kitchen table. They spoke of everything: Christmas past, little league, family relations, the hospital bill, Paul's future and his father's. They went out to eat, and his father talked throughout the whole meal, another first. He told stories of the symphony that Paul had never heard, and about his youth as an only child. His intelligence and perspective amazed Paul. He marveled that his gregarious dinner companion was the same person who had seldom even spoken for so many years.

As they entered the airport, Paul was startled. It was the hug-prone woman again. This time she was wearing a gray polyester suit and had her hair tied back in a bun. She was wearing a large silver necklace, big earrings, and a bracelet on her left arm. She did not even look in his direction. She was there to meet the morning plane, as she was everyday.

Paul stared at her, thinking, "She is just trying to get things right and hoping against all odds that this was the day Benny would arrive."

It was not. The woman gave her hug away, again to a surprised stranger. This time it was a business man arriving home, and the unknown and unknowing hugger had beaten the man's brittle wife to the greeting. Paul observed the wife's face grow taut as her worst nightmares were confirmed. She had always been afraid her husband was having an affair, and now she was sure of it. They would have some talking to do after this.

Taking a deep breath, Paul turned back to his father and said, "Good-bye". But it was more like, "Hello." There was a connection between them now, missing since the day he was born, missing also between his parents. Paul and his father loved each other and would each go on with their own lives. They were independent for the first time, not needing each other, but enjoying each other. Their hug signaled the end of a relationship of parent/child, the beginning of a friendship based on shared humanity. A tear rolled down his father's cheek as he turned to board the plane.

   After his father's visit, college changed again for Paul. His studies became effortless, and he got straight A's without even trying. He had done poorly in high school, reacting to the teachers as he had to his father. When his relationship with his father changed, so did his academic performance. There was nothing to prove and nobody to prove it to. Without any pressure at all, learning became fun and effortless.

   Paul's perception of professors had also changed. They now looked scared—afraid to leave the university, afraid to alienate students, parents, or administration. Their expertise was so small and the world so big that they had to teach the same things over and over just to provide themselves with some security. They were paid for what they knew and not what they could learn.

One guest lecturer was a noteworthy exception. Paul attended a lecture given by a man named Fernando, a linguist from Chile. In a slow, confident, and deliberate manner, the Chilean referred to men from the United States as adolescent cowboys. Then he backed up his statement by citing examples of our heroes. John Wayne, James Dean and Clint Eastwood were heroes of our times, but they lacked sensitivity. Paul listened closely as Fernando offered up new perspectives on the culture, a culture Paul was so much a part of that he had not even noticed it. During the lecture, sparked by a question from the audience, Fernando spoke of love. He had met his wife-to-be while he was in college. Upon declaring that he was in love, he had immediately stopped attending classes, living with but one purpose: to court his bride-to-be. He explained that this was normal in his culture—love comes before all else. Their courtship lasted for a year. His Latin blood rose slowly at first but finally reached a fever pitch. He thought only of his true love. They ate together, danced together, and talked together, sharing nearly every waking moment. They could not be bothered with jobs or getting an education during this time because, as Fernando said, "Our occupation was each other." They gracefully accepted and embraced the task of laying a firm foundation of love and respect to support a marriage, a bond that would last a lifetime.

When Paul attended this lecture, Fernando was in his late fifties and still married to the woman he had courted when he was eighteen. Fernando, dark eyes gleaming, declared that finding and securing his true love so early had allowed him to get on with the rest of his life. Without true love, one must muster all interest and motivation oneself; with true love as a constant companion, every moment is doubly worth living. Paul enjoyed Fernando's words, and the ideas made sense to him, but at that time only conceptually.

Paul no longer waited for weekends—every day brought him opportunities to play. Sometimes he went camping, and sometimes he went to class. Everything was fun and educational. It had been a while since he had heard the Voice, but he was so busy exploring the world around him, he didn't notice its absence until it spoke again.

Paul noted in passing that his ex-roommate Jeff hadn't gotten along with Liz any better than he had. But Paul was discovering he had more in common with the local people who went about their daily activities without much pretense. He had become friends with the two local students, Mel and Steve, who lived in the same dorm he did. Steve was memorable for his haircut, a strange affair almost shaved on the top, with wisps of hair over his ears and down the back of his neck. He looked stupid, but wasn't. Mel looked intellectual, with brown thick-rimmed glasses and a crewcut. He always carried books around, though he never read them. He was not nearly as smart as he looked.

To spice up their sorry scholastic attempts, these two would stand barefoot about ten feet apart and throw a sharp knife at each other's feet. They called this game "Chicken." Mel would throw the knife as close to Steve's feet as he could without hitting him, and Steve would throw it back at Mel's feet. Occasionally one of them would hit the other. At the first sign of blood, the game changed to one of retaliation. "I'm bleeding, what were you aiming for?"

Although he did not share their idea of fun, Paul still had something in common with Mel and Steve—he was thinking less, and enjoying more. The less he thought, the more he knew.

Steve and Mel were usually happy and easily entertained—Steve by a gallon of the cheapest grape wine he could find, and Mel with anything. He didn't even need the wine. Paul realized that complexity and simplicity in people has a lot to do with how they define their happiness. If happiness depends on listening to a Brahms Symphony, performed "just so," or winning a national Little League championship, then one is doomed to a life with very little happiness. Cheap wine and nothing are available just about anywhere.

The "bull sessions" with Mel and Steve were not exactly stimulating, but if Paul arrived already awake they were fun. Or at least weird. Like the day Paul stopped by

to find these two locals, three sheets to the wind, lighting their farts to create glowing blue flames.

On less incendiary days, Paul learned about philosophy—Mel and Steve style—or listened to stories of Gunnison's history.

The town had begun as a stage stop. A layover between Denver and Grand Junction. It was a tourist place without the trap, that is until gold was discovered.

Two brothers really built the town. They were heading west to the land of opportunity to make their fortunes when one of them got cold feet. He was the pessimist and always had been, and now he would not budge one foot further into unknown terrain. He had half a mind to go right back to Denver and open a store there. His brother could not convince him to go on, but his own adamant refusal to backtrack resulted in a compromise called Gunnison. For years the town itself never made up its mind, tugged between optimism or pessimism, future opportunities or security.

The gold strike changed all that. The kind of people who stay in one place and serve the people passing through were joined by crazy idealistic miners, thousands of them. Enough to tip the scales of the town in the direction of growth and an eye to the future. Both brothers rejoiced in the change. The pessimistic one opened a bank, to hold the money, while the optimistic one became a miner himself. He, of course, made the largest strike, became the richest man in town, and ended up owning and ranching much of the land around Gunnison.

Paul enjoyed the stories, and kept inviting Mel and Steve to go camping with him—an offer they both turned down at least as often as he made it. Neither of them could understand camping, being quite content to have a bed to sleep in and college tests to do poorly on.

It was near the end of the semester and time for final exams, but Paul was not nervous. He viewed exams as artificial constructs that appear to make one moment more important than another. He had learned that life happens when it happens, "ready or not," without regard to schedules or calendars. The idea that he could be tested more in one moment than in another seemed too ridiculous to be scary. Motivation, the kind people claim to get from deadlines or test dates, lived within him. Each moment was equally worth living to the fullest. External influences seemed artificial, and the promise of a good grade or a good job in the future didn't urge him on. He knew that delayed gratification is something invented by human beings, a joke perpetrated on themselves. There is really nothing worth waiting for, ignoring, letting go of, or holding on to.

What seemed more interesting then final exams was the week vacation following. Paul decided to go camping.

It was winter in the mountains, and although Gunnison had not received much snow, the temperature was hovering near zero. Paul packed accordingly. The same kid who had wandered off without much water on his first camping trip was now planning. He stuffed his backpack with all of his camping gear and clothing for the coldest possible conditions. He placed the rancher's key and the gunshot chip of rock from his brush with death in his pocket and strapped his sleeping bag on to his backpack. He walked toward the dormitory stairs, footsteps echoing through the empty hallways. The other students had already left, most heading home or to warm climates. Ironically, the ski slopes around Gunnison would soon be filled with visiting college kids, many from warm climates. The hope for satisfaction always seemed to reside someplace else.

Liz was going to New Orleans for winter break, and Jeff was probably drinking somewhere. Mel and Steve were going home—across-town. Paul was on his way down the last flight of stairs, fully braced and prepared for the rigors of winter camping. He never made it out of the dorm.

On the third step from the bottom, he stopped short, stalled. There were just three more short steps to take before reaching the door, but Paul had not mentally anticipated leaving. Usually he would have been thinking ahead, living in the future with his expectations, thinking of his camping trip while still on the stairs. Not this time. His body was on the third step from the bottom, eight feet from the winter chill, and so was his mind.

There had been times in his life when his mind and body were so far apart they weren't even on speaking terms. He had run a marathon, 26 miles and 385 yards, without even training. By ignoring his body, his mind finished the race in under four hours, but it took over a year for his body to get over the pain he had suppressed to finish the race. The ache in his ankles and calves was a constant reminder of the marathon for many months afterward. And then there was eating, a true split between mind and body. His mind would want the whole apple pie while his body was already full with one piece, his mind saying, "Yes," and his body screaming, "No." As recently as planning his trip to Gunnison, Paul had spent hours thinking about going away to college, before he had even bought the plane ticket.

The old Paul had wanted to be prepared so badly he'd spent more time in the future than the present. The new Paul was on the third step from the bottom when he heard the Voice say, "Stop." He stopped.

He stayed poised, ready to go down, go up, or remain on the third step forever. His mind was calm. He waited for what seemed like hours. The request to fall off the cliff had been dramatic; this command to stop was much more subtle.

Finally, the Voice spoke again, but in a different tone. It said, "You may go."

For a moment there was a strange confusion, then his body danced down the remaining stairs. The performance included two impossible jumps and a kind of tipsy scarecrow near-fall that brought his head within inches of the floor. Looking closer, he discovered that his body was not touching the floor at all. Relieved of the weight of his mind, his body was so light it levitated. It turned, waved, and floated right through the closed door.

"Amazing! Impossible!" Paul thought. This was too weird for what was left of him to make sense of. He hadn't known his body could perform such acrobatics, or walk through closed doors. He had always believed his body stopped him from doing such things. Perhaps he had confused the mind with the body, and the body with the mind. Limitations, it appeared, were only a phantom of the mind. As a fictional entity, the mind could no more have real limitations and problems than could Pinocchio.

"Is it possible my mind creates stories that limit the movement of my body?" Paul wondered.

He decided that later, if his mind rejoined his body, he would try walking through some closed doors. For now, he could not walk anywhere. He had no legs, no body at all. He had spent his whole life attempting to be some-body and ended up, at least for now, being no-body.

In philosophy he had studied the mind-body problem, but had never expected such a dramatic illustration.

His body, it seemed, had gone camping while his mind had stayed home. Or his body had not gone camping at all and was lounging in a cheap room at the Gunnison Hotel watching "Father Knows Best" and eating corn chips. There was no way to tell. He was used to his mind wandering, but he'd never expected his body to wander off without him.

"No body!" his mind screamed.

Paul began to realize how much time he spent eating, sleeping, going to the toilet, and bathing. It appeared his mind did not require such maintenance. He pondered the strange relationship he had with his body. Mind wants a piece of lemon chiffon pie, so body eats it. Mind wants to go camping or run a marathon, so body obliges. His mind dictated, and his body did its best to obey. "What, indeed, was the relationship between the two?" Paul asked nobody.

It appeared that his body was nothing but a well-trained companion (man's best friend) to his mind (a fictional entity). The mind needs a consistent story line to prove its existence, something which can never be proved. Proving something that is not true does not make it true, and no amount of evidence for the existence of the mind makes it real. However, the body, brain included, cannot avoid evidence. The body dances with evidence while the mind manufactures it. When the body has to deal with the manufactured evidence, illusion is born, and the map takes the place of the territory.

"But my mind controls my body," Paul's mind spoke authoritatively.

He had been taught that bodies are our connection with the world. Bodies keep our feet on the ground both literally and figuratively. Feet can be in only one place at a time while minds can be anywhere. The mind thinks ahead, while the body lags behind; at least, that was how it had appeared. Paul would think of a project, completing it in his head before he could even buy the necessary supplies. By the time his body was engaged in the project, his mind would be on to something else. He wondered if having a good relationship between mind and body might require them both to be in the same place at the same time.

The graceful movements his body had performed as it left the dormitory suggested that rigidity and aging had nothing to do with the body. There was his, making impossible movements—impossible, according to his mind. He had pictured himself floating through closed doors, but had never thought it could be done. He suspected that getting old physically required a cooperation between the mind and the body.

"Perhaps we only age because we think we will age."

If aging was only a habit, then talking about aging was a fairy tale passed on as common wisdom from one generation to the next. The telling of this tale resulted in jealousy between age and youth, producing both a generation gap and aging.

If the apparent limitations of Paul's body were in fact limitations of his mind, then what really were the limitations of his body? Until recently, he had never seen anything he had not expected to see, felt anything he had not expected to feel, or heard anything he had not expected to hear. He had lived trapped in his mind, unable to recognize anything that could not make sense to him. And he had learned his limitations well. His body might have walked around a unicorn, his mind oblivious.

Now he realized that he'd limited himself with "things." Things that he thought were true, but were not. Things that were true, but he couldn't believe. So he'd created the everyday illusion called life. This illusion was shattered when he first heard the Voice.

His mind was obviously a result of the Voice: a kind of personalization of its universal messages. The less he personalized the Voice, the more accurate was his thinking, and the more intuitive he became.

His body, at least to some extent, was also the direct result of the Voice. First his mind and body had split; now there seemed to be a different split taking place. Paul's mind seemed to be splitting—as in the splitting headache of the aspirin ads. He was about to explore the difference between perception and thought. A difference that seemed too small to explore until his mind stretched and he witnessed himself adding meaning to his perceptions. There

was a huge difference between what he perceived and the thoughts and judgments he had about those perceptions. The two were never the same, but Paul had seldom noticed the difference between them.

As a young child he used his body as a delightful tool for exploring the world. Like the wet warmth of bathtime as a two-year-old. The bar of soap, the rubber toys, and the stream of water from the faucet were unlimited worlds for exploration. He did not really know what a bath was, so it could be anything. He felt the embracing water making him lighter. Accidentally dunking under the water, hearing his laughter echo off the white walls of the bathtub, and chasing a slippery bar of soap were all delightful experiences. He played in the bath forever, which for his mother was about twenty minutes. As a two year old, he lived in the moment—where he was and what he was doing was his whole world. Each experience was not even his universe, but *the* universe.

As he got older, culture made sure he developed understanding and the need to control his experiences. The easiest way was to split life into separate worlds. Bathtime was for cleaning, and swinging was for play, which had to be earned or deserved. Everything had to have a purpose.

School had certain parameters and thus became a world onto itself. Paul learned how to divide before he learned how to add, as we all do. We start out as the whole universe, and then divide things into bite-sized pieces, and then spend our lives trying to get things back together.

By age six, Paul had many individual worlds, which he had to lump together into one box. At first they did not fit very well. Some of his worlds stuck out, and the experiences that did not fit into the box at all were eventually forgotten. It had taken some time, but Paul had managed to force all of his unique worlds, results of his early division lessons, into one. The process was called "growing up." Naming and identifying were the main techniques for fitting the different worlds together. Once Paul had labeled it, he could put an experience wherever he wanted and tell it to stay there. And it usually did. If he was unable to make sense of an experience, he would apply his next technique: *act as if* everything is under control.

"The final blow!" Paul realized now.

Those key words, *act as if*, had allowed him to stop using his senses and begin his acting career. He became an actor bent on playing a role. The trick to life became discovering what was expected of him just in time to pretend that he knew it all along.

The world according to his senses was put aside, leaving room for his world of illusion. Judgments protectively surrounded his self-contained world, his self-controlled world. "But what do I control?" he asked himself.

Ignoring his body's senses had reduced possible conflict with the imaginary world created by his mind.

What had looked so real to him before was obviously illusion. Now, suddenly, Paul could see the make-believe world created by his mind and its judgments. His body did not need to be in service to his thoughts.

"Freedom!" Paul did not need to be in control of anything ever again.

He plunged back into the judgment-free infinite pleasures of a two-year-old's experiences. In the world of his senses and his body there was real excitement, joy, and life. Each experience, every moment, again became a discovery. He cried, without tears, mourning that "growing up" loss of his body.

With a jolt, Paul remembered he was now no-body. His bodiless mind still hovered on the dormitory stairway.

And the door below him was opening. Someone or something was entering this thoughtful stairwell.

Was he about to be saved?...Found out?...Captured?...Or missed entirely? Was there even a self here to be noticed at all?

The door opened. Paul's body looked up toward his mind.

His head was upside down near the doorknob, and his knees were curled over the top of the door. His body was smiling—a Cheshire smile, like the one weeks before on the edge of the cliff. Then his body vanished and the door closed.

His body was playing, without the anchor of his mind to hold it down. Anything and everything seemed possible.

The door started to open again. This time Paul was ready. He was not sure how it would look without a mouth, but his mind prepared the best smile it could, by thinking light, happy thoughts.

Cautiously, someone dressed completely in black entered the stairwell. His face was smudged with make-up as black as chimney soot. In spite of the outfit, Paul recognized Steve. Could a whole week have passed already? It seemed as though spring break had just started. Steve looked more like he was returning from a burglar's convention than returning to college.

"What can he be up to?" thought Paul.

Steve passed directly through Paul's mind and made his way up the stairs.

Paul, certain that he would see his own body at the door again, had not been ready for Steve. Otherwise, he might have tried to speak to him. Steve, intent on stealth, had not even noticed Paul's smile.

"What *was* he up to?" Maybe Steve and Mel had returned to the dorm to play, spending their vacation on campus in a game of army, sneaking around in pursuit of each other.

Paul did not have long to ponder. Steve was sneaking back down the stairs, looking like some kind of anti-Santa with a big cloth bag flung over his back and a clock radio under his arm. Had he had gone to his room to pack a few things for home? No, he'd been robbing dorm rooms. If Steve had his own clock radio, he wouldn't have been late for class all the time.

Paul wondered what to do. Steve had passed through his mind on the way up the stairs, but Paul suspected that there could be a way to stop Steve before he slipped out the door. But how? Paul couldn't speak, so he tried thinking to Steve. Just as Steve reached the bottom step, Paul remembered the game of "Red light, Green light" he had played as a child.

Paul concentrated. "Red light." Steve froze in his tracks. His mouth didn't move, but his mind asked, "Who's there?"

"Red light" had worked! Paul added, "This is your conscience speaking. You must put the things back."

Steve looked shocked. He sighed deeply, then swung the bag off of his shoulder and sat on the bottom step, the clock radio still clutched under his left arm. Right elbow on his knee and chin resting on his hand, he adopted the pose of The Thinker.

Thinking, for Steve, was a bit like attempting a foreign language. Paul was surprised by how little there was going on in Steve's head. There were no communication barriers between their minds.

Steve thought, "I won't put the stuff back. I want it."

"Those things aren't yours, big boy," Paul thought.

Steve whined, "But I never get what I want! These kids are so spoiled, with so many things. They won't mind if I take these."

"It's not those students I'm concerned about—it's you. Sure, they'll be upset at first, but they'll soon forget it and buy new toys. Probably better ones. You, on the other hand, will never forget that you took these things.

Never do anything you don't want to remember forever. You can forget what you want to remember, but you will always remember what you want to forget."

Paul was having a good time, invisible and playing the part of another person's conscience. Playing someone else's conscience was something he often did without knowing it. Like his fantasies of being invisible and watching people without their knowing. Though Steve was neither feminine nor pretty enough to fulfill the fantasies, Paul was having fun.

Steve mumbled to himself, "I didn't even know I had a conscience before tonight." He rose slowly, exhausted from the conversation, turned, and trudged back up the stairs. It seemed to take much longer for him to return the things than it had to steal them. After awhile Steve wandered back down the stairs, obviously confused, with a large empty sack over his shoulder.

Paul thought, "If my mind and body ever get back together I will give Steve a clock radio as a present."

Steve had presented Paul with the opportunity to do a good deed. Paul owed Steve a debt of gratitude.

Paul had communicated with Steve so easily, and not a word had been spoken. His mind was beginning to enjoy its bodiless existence. It is no accident that we have both mind and body, but somehow losing his body had set Paul's mind free. Poised in the dormitory stairwell, his mind was active. Without a body, it did not differentiate between waking and sleep. His relationship with time and activities changed. With no body, he had nothing to do, no actions. There was more to this mind-body duality than he had imagined, or could imagine, until his body was at least near his mind again.

Paul's mind took trips down memory lane. Some were directed by his own thoughts, others inspired and guided by the Voice. His past came back to him in three-dimensional, lifelike detail. Sometimes it seemed as if he was transported through time, experiencing the smells, tastes, sounds, pictures and feelings of each memory. At other times he was like a spectator with a front row seat, watching scenes from his life as if they were happening right now, right in front of him.

Paul, a child at play with colored wooden blocks in the living room of his home on Kinnecott Street. Pudgy little hands reached for the blocks, all of the blocks, even though they could only hold one at a time. "Gurgle, Goo." The sheer pleasure of making sounds, no worry about producing words. Lying on his back, Paul basked in the sweet smell of baby powder, the softness of his mother's hands applying it. Paul, on his belly in the middle of the floor, now saw his mother sitting on the couch watching him, loving him, her hands busy knitting with brightly-colored yarn.

Paul saw this scene first as an observer, then through his little one-year-old eyes, and finally from his mother's perspective. Each view was different, though

the scene was the same. While he played on the floor with the blocks, making towers by piling two and sometimes three wooden blocks on top of each other, there was the rhythmic clicking of his mother's knitting needles. As his perspective changed and he observed the same scene through the eyes of his mother, he no longer heard the clicking of the knitting needles or saw the blocks. She was looking only at him, listening to his sounds, thinking of her love for him. He knocked over a tower, shouting and laughing. His mother stopped knitting, leaned over and rubbed his back, momentarily distracting him from the blocks. They focused on each other. She had a wonderful relaxed smile on her big face, the most familiar face in the world to Paul, much more familiar than his own. As an observer, he saw this snapshot: the loving connection between a mother and child.

After reviewing this memory, Paul wondered if he would ever be a father and love his child as much as his mother loved him. He did not hear the Voice directly, but it gave the answer: "Yes."

His mind skipped among memories. *Toys. Balls. Tennis.*

Suddenly he was playing the climatic match of his high school tennis career. He felt the racket in his hand and the sweat on his back and chest, cooling him as a breeze blew. He watched the ball intently. *Smack.* It hit his racket. His hand shifted grip from forehand to backhand. He bounced on his toes, ready to run to the net if he got a chance. Between points, Paul looked over at his opponent, who was obviously angry, mouth drawn tight, concentrating too hard, forgetting to have fun.

From his opponent's perspective, there was no anger, only depression as he thought, "I can't beat this guy! The coach is going to yell at me again. Why did I go out for tennis anyway?"

There were people on the bleachers, each with a different perspective. Some did not even see the ball, or Paul. As he adopted each person's perspective, he discovered what was important to them at the moment. A guy in the front row was hearing his math professor lecture about square roots earlier that day. One of Paul's teammates looked more attentive, but he was busy overhearing a conversation between two cheerleaders sitting behind him. Most of the crowd was thinking about things that had happened in school that day. Two sweethearts in the top row were thinking only of each other.

Reliving this experience with complete sensory awareness while watching himself without reference to a specific location made Paul dizzy at first, but he soon adapted to it. His mind was able to do all of this while it remained hovering in the stairwell.

Many more memories flashed by for review. Paul did some "housecleaning" by adding new perspectives to old situations and then storing the experiences in his memory with updated wisdom. "My past can only haunt me if I limit myself to one perspective of each experience,"

he realized. He viewed and altered his past, and during the process changed some sad memories to happy ones.

He tried to see future memories, but was met by darkness each time. Paul wondered if he would ever be able to see the future, and if he could be trusted to do so. For now, the past was plenty interesting.

And amusing. Like his first "real" date. Pat, a cheerleader from another high school, was sitting next to him in the back seat of a friend's car. They were on the way to a dance, and he was embarrassed, uncomfortable, and preoccupied. He did not know if Pat liked him or how much he liked her. She looked younger than he remembered her. He was surprised at his own boldness as he leaned forward to kiss her; he had not even remembered doing that. In the next moment, he understood why he had not remembered it—she turned away. Paul had been rejected, and the moment was lost. But even though the memory was buried, he had learned to be more cautious, to take fewer risks in the future.

Now, watching the scene, Paul noticed something new. What he'd seen as rejection at the time was really Pat leaning over to retrieve a bobby pin that had fallen to the floor. He had jumped to a conclusion, something he did often.

How many other times had he made decisions based on a limited perspective? He was about to count the times he could remember, but realized that he did not have any fingers to count on. What could he count on? What indeed?

His question was answered indirectly by the Voice as it said, "Prepare yourself."

Paul's body was at the door.

This time it knocked and waited for an invitation to enter. Paul was beginning to discover the sense of humor his body contained, and becoming aware of the seriousness of his mind. He thought, "Come in," and his body floated through the door, sat down on the first step and mimicked Steve's "Thinker" position.

Paul was pleased to have his body back in the vicinity of his mind, anxious to have the two reunited. His body had obviously been aware of everything that had happened here in its absence. It was no accident that his body had taken The Thinker position, a posture Paul never adopted. His favorite position for thinking had always been lying back on the floor with his legs resting on a chair.

Paul felt suddenly awkward. Like meeting a person who looks exactly like you. In this case, the person was Paul, and yet completely separate from him, sitting two steps away.

As his mind spoke, the words came out of his body's mouth. Paul had always enjoyed ventriloquists, but this was too much.

Communication was weirdly cumbersome at first, as his mind spoke through his body and his body thought through his mind. His body and mind had missed each other. As his mother often said, "Absence makes the heart grow fonder." Paul's mind eagerly received thoughts of his body's adventures, in vivid detail. First he was floating up to the top of the dormitory building. Suddenly he was floating all the way to the top of the World Trade Center, then standing there looking down on New York, the Statue of Liberty appearing no bigger than a little girl coming home from school. He felt the gentle swaying of the building, one of the biggest cities in the world at his feet, and watched an airplane fly by below him.

His mind thought for his body, and his body spoke for his mind. Which was Paul, he wondered, mind or body? Zen had prepared him for the paradox that he was both mind and body, and neither mind or body. There was both separation and no-separation at the same time.

His body and mind continued conversing with each other in this unusual way. His body had a lot to communicate. It had been ignored for a long time, only receiving attention from his mind when its pain or the pleasure was great enough. Paul realized that his thoughts had become so important he'd lost contact with the wisdom of the body.

His mind was a little miffed that it had not been with his body when it stood on the top of the World Trade Center. In the past, he had always considered his mind limited by the physical limitations of his body, but now he became aware that his body was weighed down by the imaginary limitations of his mind. Relieved of the constraints of his mind, his body had taken advantage of the opportunity to enjoy adventures beyond his wildest dreams. Now, as his body and mind communicated, Paul began to think that anything was possible.

This idea would soon be challenged repeatedly.

Anything meant anything he could imagine, and much more. His mind did not yet have a way of reaching outside of his imagination, but his body was beginning to lead him outside these invisible boundaries.

Astronomers say the universe is expanding at high velocity. Paul's world was certainly expanding at an incredible pace. He realized that what was being taught at college, or in any classroom, was an accounting of our current accepted limitations: a report of where someone has stopped learning about something.

He wondered if there was a crossover point at which what is known is slightly larger than what there is yet to learn. How far from that point might humans be?

A person is called a good plumber when he or she knows enough about plumbing to install a faucet, fix a leaky pipe, or stop a dripping shower head. "What system of measurement do we use to decide when to call a person a good human being? How do we determine the quality of a person and the quality of life?" Paul wondered. For lack of a better system, perhaps human beings

began to measure wealth and intelligence to judge other people and to guide themselves.

Paul—his mind hovering above the third step of the dormitory stairs, his body two steps below—was lost in the wonders of the universe. His body cleared its throat, and his mind said, "How about joining me again?"

The response popped into his mind. "I thought you'd never ask! But first an apology is in order."

Without hesitation his mind said via his body, "I am sorry for both the abuse and neglect that I have heaped on you. I thank you for your willingness to function so well in spite of my unappreciative mind."

His body sent the thought, "That all sounds well and good, but an apology is not an apology without some promise about our future together."

Again his mind spoke through his body: "I promise that from this day forward I will do my best to attend to the wisdom of my body. I will give at least as much attention to my physical senses as I give to my thoughts."

"That too sounds good, but it doesn't give me anything I can count on."

"I promise I will run no more marathons. I will soak in a long, hot bath at least once a week, particularly if I don't think I have time to do so. I will get a full body massage at least twice a month, and I will do my best to pay attention to my body if and when I have sex, instead of just my brain."

At the utterance of those words, his body floated up to rejoin his mind. It was a union similar to a marriage: two separate entities becoming one. Body and mind, reunited, could do and think things that were beyond what either could achieve separately.

The search for the right person to marry would be easier if it began with the marrying of the mind and body of the searcher. Often, what the mind wants is so different from what the body wants that the two are in conflict. Many species on Earth are spared this conflict—their union between mind and body are intact from birth to death. Their brains contain the necessary programming for them to be foxes, deer, or turnips, and they lack the evolutionary development of a mind. This reunion of Paul's mind and body was a step toward being complete and whole within himself.

Paul turned and bounded up the dormitory steps five at a time, something which was clearly impossible. He was just seconds ahead of the first group of students arriving back from semester break. From inside his dorm room, he could hear the familiar sounds of voices, laughter, and the banging of doors.

He'd missed his planned vacation, but now Paul was whole, much more than the sum of his parts. The students in the hallway exclaimed about fantastic beaches and parties and skiing, but he doubted any of their experiences could rival his adventures right here in the dorm.

Crash. The door burst open.

Paul spun around, ready for any impossible visitation, ready even for the Voice incarnate, ready for miracles.

It was only the old rancher, looking dusty and very ordinary. He sauntered into the dorm room, put his finger to his mouth, and whispered, "Hushhhhhh."

Then he headed directly over to Jeff's bed, or what had been Jeff's bed, and lay down. Within seconds he began snoring. He slept on his side, with his small weathered frame turned away from Paul, looking more like a child than an adult.

Paul blinked. He considered waking the old man, but instead sat down on his own bed and meditated. In the past, he had so much to think about; now he wanted only *to be*. He acquainted himself with his body, beginning at his feet and working his way up to his head. The whole process took about an hour. He resolved to have the first of many long hot baths that evening and to find a massage therapist the next day.

Paul got up, mind and body, pulled on his shoes and started for the door, deciding to leave the rancher asleep in his room. Quick as a wink, the rancher got up and followed him into the hall before Paul could close the door. The rancher followed Paul down the steps and out the dormitory door.

Paul realized he had been without food or water for over a week. He was hungry. He said, "Well, old-timer, how about you and I go get something to eat?"

The rancher obviously heard him but did not reply. He pointed toward his battered old pickup truck. The rancher sat down on the passenger's side, so Paul got in the driver's side door. He started the truck, and they were on their way. The rancher navigated by pointing, and they ended up at a local greasy spoon.

Paul had a great breakfast, which at this restaurant was a miracle. He had done the impossible again. Not only did the rancher not eat, but the waitress treated him as if he was not even there. Paul paid the bill, and they were off. Back inside the truck, Paul said, "Now where to, old-timer?"

He directed Paul to the Gunnison Hardware Store. Once inside, the rancher was in his element. Like a kid in

a toy store, he examined every gun in the store—about a hundred—pulled down old dusty boxes of nuts and screws, and wound up infant toys near the front of the store.

Paul surveyed the store walls. They were covered with shelves holding everything from stuffed gophers to electric drills. Paul didn't even recognize some of the odd gizmos. His gaze found something familiar, a clock radio just like the one Steve had been carrying on the stairs. Paul purchased the radio and, upon the insistence of the rancher, forty feet of rope, a used Remington twenty-two, and some shells. The gun was a single-shot with bolt action, and it cost fifteen dollars. Paul had no idea why the rancher needed the gun and the rope. The clerk seemed to approve of the purchases, eyeing the Remington single-shot in particular. Like the waitress, the clerk also ignored the rancher. A pattern was beginning to develop. Paul wondered if the rancher had offended the people in town. He was quiet, to be sure, but good company, and he knew a good rifle when he saw one.

The moment they got back to Paul's dorm room, the old man returned to bed and promptly started snoring. Paul had imagined possible roommates, but none of his pictures included a short old rancher with a long beard and a mat of dirty gray hair. The rancher looked like the Marlboro man grown old and shrunken.

Paul got used to the old guy over the next week, because the rancher followed him everywhere, like a shadow, except that he was around even in the dark. At night, the rancher led Paul around town, apparently to his favorite places. Paul quickly learned the seedy side of Gunnison. He discovered there was a regular, big stakes, poker game at the Mayor's house each Wednesday night. He also learned that behind the dry-goods store there was a small, out-of-the-way bar where the locals met to talk about the old days. The conversation quickly dried up when Paul walked in, but this was the only place where a few patrons acknowledged or spoke to the rancher. Two old prospectors in the corner shared a drink and conversation with the rancher, but not until Paul moved beyond hearing range.

Like Mary's little lamb, the rancher followed Paul to school each day. He even took notes in some of the classes, though he would never let Paul see them. The old man insisted on having a new pencil and a pad of paper at each class. Again, none of the students acknowledged the rancher's presence, and none of the teachers ever called on him.

After Paul's last class on Friday, the rancher pointed toward the dorm room. Once there, the rancher slept while Paul packed camping supplies. As Paul headed toward the door, the rancher got up and checked to make sure the gun and rope had been packed. Before heading out of the dorm, they put the clock radio in Steve's room, without a note. Steve always left the door unlocked, figuring he had nothing worth protecting. Paul imagined the look on

Steve's face when he discovered the radio, and decided
never to tell Steve the radio was from him. Perhaps Steve
would think his conscience had given him a present.

They left the dorm, hopped into the pickup truck,
and headed for the hills with Paul in the driver's seat again
and the rancher giving directions. He directed Paul down
backroads and paths that may have been roads at one time,
but had not been used or maintained for many years. They
bounced around in the cab of the truck, so old it had no
seat belts.

Paul drove for an hour as the rancher silently
pointed the way. They rode through some of the most
rugged country Paul had ever seen. Through old dry
stream beds, and some not so dry. They went up mountains that looked much too steep to climb. Their drive
took them to the bottom of a canyon about a half mile
long, sheer cliffs rising on either side. The width of the
canyon gave no more than six inches clearance on either
side of the truck. Paul left the rear view mirrors at the
beginning of that canyon. It had taken some coaxing to
get him into the canyon, but once inside, he was committed to drive all the way to the other side. There was no
way to back out or escape from the truck without break-
ing either the front windshield or the back window. Paul
drove as carefully as he could, but still hit the sides three
or four times. The rancher did not seem to mind.

The drive through the canyon took them to the
end of their journey. Paul stopped the truck on a small

plateau and they got out, skirted a cliff, and began climbing on foot. They came to a narrow ridge with a cliff on the other side. The rancher indicated he would hold the rope while Paul climbed over the ridge and down the cliff. Paul thought better of this plan—not that he didn't trust the rancher, but his recent experiences had taught him to be a bit more careful. He found a suitable boulder and fastened the rope securely. He offered to let the rancher go first, but the rancher declined with a shake of his head.

Paul grabbed the rope and took a deep breath, bracing for the descent. It was only about a twenty-five foot drop to the valley floor below. Paul started down. His hands burned as he backed hand over hand down the rope. Sliding as little as possible, he locked his feet around the rope to take some of the weight off his aching hands. Finally Paul reached the bottom, sweating, hands blistering.

He looked up, waiting to see the rancher sliding down the rope. He gave a tug on the rope, expecting to feel the rancher tug back, but instead the rope came tumbling down on him, bringing some pebbles with it. At the end was a big granny knot.

Paul gawked up at the sheer cliff. He called up to the rancher. No answer. Paul felt a sinking sensation in the pit of his stomach. Beads of sweat trickled down his face. Something was wrong, horribly wrong. He was standing in a cleft a hundred feet across, next to a rock wall he couldn't climb. Along the wall were several large boulders, some of them just taller than he was. He stepped

around the closest one and gasped. The body of the rancher lay prone and still on the ground.

The smell hit Paul. The rancher must have been lying there for a week. In shock, Paul stared. Then gasped and jumped back. The rancher's arm was moving. The body extended its index finger, beckoning Paul closer.

Paul took a deep breath and wished he hadn't. He reluctantly moved closer to the rancher. The stench was awful. He covered his mouth and nose with his shirt before kneeling at the rancher's side. The dead man rolled over to face Paul, and his breath brought tears to Paul's eyes. Paul blinked and shook his head to clear it.

"What took you so long?" the rancher said. "I'm becoming plant food."

He was right. He looked a bit more like a vegetable, on its way to becoming a mineral, than an animal.

"I'm sorry it took so long to get here," Paul said. "But, I didn't know where I was going. Anyway, you were with me."

"In mind only!" the rancher snorted. "Last Sunday morning I fell off this cliff. Not much of a fall, but I landed wrong. Broke my darned neck straight away. Never even felt it. But I had one last thought. 'Maybe I could have a few more days on Earth, some way or other.'" The rancher tilted his moldering head around curiously. "Then my mind up and left my body. Ran off to fetch you, knowing somehow you understood this 'mind and body' stuff.

Guess I wasn't too talkative, but if you'd of tuned in to my thoughts, you'd of known what was going on."

"I didn't think of it," Paul admitted. Could he have done it? Realizing that he was not sure he knew how to. While he had been politely waiting for his silent visitor to speak, Paul had forgotten to listen for the rancher's thoughts.

"Well, young fella, have you got the rifle and the key?"

"Yes," Paul said, sliding off his backpack, relieved to have something concrete to do. He had the rifle strapped to the side of his pack. The key was in the front pocket, along with an unfinished postcard to his parents.

The ranchers face, peeling as if from a wicked sunburn, managed a smile. It was grotesque, but obviously the best he could do.

Paul, trying not to flinch, helped the rancher to his feet.

The dead man took the gun and held it stiffly to his shoulder, aiming at an imaginary target. "Nice feel to it," he said.

Paul held out the key and the rancher looked at it thoughtfully.

"Keep that key and take good care of it!" the rancher ordered. "You'll need it one of these days."

Paul found himself mustering a surreal politeness. "Is there something I can do for you? Can I rush you to

the hospital? I'm not sure how we can get you out of this valley, but we can try."

"Ya darned fool! I don't need a hospital," the rancher produced a rattling chuckle. "Hospitals are for folks who are still alive. I died a week ago." Laying a crumbling hand on Paul's shoulder, he said, "You already done what I wanted. Thanks for the gun, and thanks for coming. Guess I should thank you for the little bit of a college education you exposed me to, but I got to say I didn't catch much point to it. I haven't got much time left, so go ahead and ask me those questions you're trying not to ask."

The ranchers stench was getting worse, and Paul figured the old man's time had already run out. But he'd put up with the smell for a chance to talk to a dead man who was willing to talk with him. Paul blurted out, "What's it like being dead? Is there a heaven? What has the process of death taught you?"

"Whoa! Not so fast, there. One question at a time is all I can answer—after all, I'm dead." The rancher sat down on the ground, stiff legs sticking straight out in front of him. He said, "Death isn't that different from life. I always figured it would be, but it isn't. I don't get hungry, but I can still enjoy the finer things like a bright sunny day or a good gun."

He shrugged. "One odd thing. I seem to be taking an interest in horticulture. Guess it comes from turning into fertilizer!" he chuckled. "There is nothing to worry about any more. Since I died, all I can do is observe. There is no future, no past, no worries. Just death. But somehow death isn't dirty, not the end. I feel a little like laundry hung out on the line to dry. I'm just kind of waving in the breeze, happy as you please. What was your next question?"

"Is there a heaven? What have you learned from death?"

"Well, there might be a heaven and there might be a hell, but I can't see either from here, and I still got pretty good eyesight. When I was alive I suspected there were such places as New York and Singapore, but I never saw them—just postcards. I don't see any evidence for heaven or hell. But, as a dead man, I can tell you that it doesn't seem like there needs to be either. People who are alive need to have a heaven and hell just to keep themselves in line. If I find out later that there is a heaven, I will try and get word back to you."

Paul could only nod.

The rancher continued, "I haven't learned much from my death. But I didn't learn much from life either. It might be different with you. Like they say, 'You die as you lived.'"

To punctuate his quotation, he fired the rifle for the first and last time. Where he got the bullet, Paul had no idea.

"I never did any military service, but when a soldier dies, they give him a twenty-one gun salute. I deserve at least a twenty-two caliber salute."

The rancher laughed one last time. His laughter tore across the valley and echoed through Paul's ears, sounding like someone ripping very brittle newspaper into a microphone with extreme amplification.

A seductive female voice spoke through the dying echoes. "It is time to go."

The rancher lay down, gave Paul one last grizzly smile, and closed his eyes. His body slowly crumbled to a powdery mixture like that of fine dirt. All he left behind was the recently fired rifle with a spent shell in the chamber.

    "It was a dark and stormy night. Not nearly as stormy as it was dark, but stormy enough. It was the kind of a night that only ambulance drivers, pizza delivery people, and thieves are out on. Josh was the latter. There is only one thing worse than an old thief, and that is a new thief. Josh, planning his first burglary, had completely forgotten about the weather. He had planned his break-in for Tuesday night and when Tuesday night rolled around he would keep to his schedule rain or shine, though it never shined at night."

For the first time, Paul understood why teachers deserved more pay. Anyone who had to read such papers from students like Steve could not be paid enough money.

The assignment was to write a story exploring the character of one person. The fictional piece was to be concise and playful.

Steve was sitting in the front row composing his story, and Paul, still musing over his experience with the dead rancher, was sitting in the third row reading Steve's mind. Paul had always carefully chosen which books he would read because they influenced him so deeply. Now he had a new dilemma—whose mind to read. He'd discovered that by focusing on people, he could know what they were thinking. He toyed with the idea of reading every mind in the class and grabbing a paragraph from each person; then mixing and matching them.

He did preview a number of other stories just for fun. The plain girl in the back row, wearing a plaid skirt and thick glasses, was writing about endless love. The skinny guy in the front row, next to Steve, was writing about winning the Mr. Nude Galaxy Contest. Paul's mind wandered around the room, then back to Steve. He was still writing about Josh: Josh had an attack of conscience after performing his burglary and had to break back into the house to return everything he had stolen. Soon Steve would get to the part about the clock radio.

Paul thought about using some of his recent experiences for his essay. Surely they would seem like fiction to the teacher, perhaps stretching fantasy a bit too far, all the way to reality.

The clock radio: an idea whose time had come.

Living in the land of tradition and honor was Shinichi Ono, an electronics assembly-line worker. In the Japanese plant, the workers had been putting in overtime for three months, producing record numbers of clock radios, and still there were more orders coming in. He was exasperated by the repetition of his job. Grab a speaker with left hand, pick up a screw with the magnetic screwdriver with right hand, set speaker on panel, place screw into slot, turn screwdriver four times, grab speaker with left hand, grab screw with…

During an afternoon break, Shinichi Ono came up with an idea to make his job more interesting. He decided to combine his passion for writing with his displeasure for assembly line work.

Shinichi decided to place a fortune inside each clock radio.

Unlike the short, vague, impersonal notes found in Chinese fortune cookies, Shinichi wrote prose. His stories depicted people fulfilling their dreams of love and adventure, trusting their experiences to teach themselves respect and honor. Writing the fortunes gave Shinichi a new outlook on life. He spent his time away from the plant composing fortunes onto five-inch square sheets of paper, occasionally complemented by an original illustration. Shinichi carefully folded each fortune, origami style, down to the size of a postage stamp.

This innocent hobby allowed Shinichi to retain an interest in a job he did not like. Little did he know that it would also change his life forever. The particular fortune that turned the tide for both Shinichi and Lisa, a sweet young American, had mistakenly included Shinichi Ono's name and address on a return address sticker.

Lisa received a new clock radio as a birthday present from her mother. It

was attractive, with big digital numbers, but the radio sounded muffled and
distant. Luckily, Shinichi had placed
the fortune, their fortune, near the
speaker, and the paper vibrated every
time the radio played.

Disregarding the warning, "This
unit contains no owner serviceable
parts," Lisa bravely unscrewed the back
panel and removed the outer plastic
shell. She found the fortune wedged
behind the speaker and wrote to Shinichi
the next day.

After a torrid postal romance, Lisa
left America to begin a new life in
Japan, as Mrs. Shinichi Ono. Although
Shinichi was convinced it was all an
accident, the "fortune" he'd written
foretold a different story. The es-
sence of his fortune was that an American woman and a humble Japanese man
would be drawn together by the forces
of the universe. They would fall in
love and…

Shinichi and Lisa had three beautiful, healthy children. Their life
together was like a fairy tale, filled

with love, honor, and respect.   They
all lived happily ever after.

The teacher loved Paul's essay.

After class, Steve suggested Paul join him in the student union for a cup of tea. Steve often invited him to do such things, and Paul always declined in a polite and friendly manner. This time, for some reason, he accepted. Steve, looking stunned, led the way toward the union before Paul had a chance to change his mind.

As they passed the girls' dormitory, Steve told Paul there was a small group of students meeting at the union to discuss a camping excursion the following weekend. Good old Steve, always baffled by the very notion of camping, had fallen in love with Emily, a girl from Minnesota who loved to camp. All of a sudden, Steve understood camping.

Paul had not been to the union in months, but nothing had changed. Same stale air, same students. What was new was his ability to read peoples' minds. He had soon discovered that much of what a person thinks in any given day is repetitious and uninteresting. All human beings were probably originally able to mind-read, but gave up the practice out of boredom. The number of people who dwell on the same thought over and over again amazed Paul. Wanting to know what another person is thinking had provided an exciting mystery; actually knowing what other people are thinking was about as exciting as listening to last week's weather report.

Paul quickly discovered that the way people think rather than *what they think* determines who they are. There was a short blond girl standing near the door of the union thinking in a loud male voice, probably her father's voice. As she talked to herself, Paul winced at the volume and tone of her internal voice. Paul skipped several people and focused on a guy standing next to a wall of vending machines, buying cigarettes. He had pictures in his head of a cool, snowy brook in the mountains—the current billboard advertising Salem cigarettes.

Everyone Paul observed had some combination of pictures, sounds, and feelings that composed their thinking. The qualities of the pictures, sounds, and feelings determined how their day was going. Paul saw a young man sitting alone in the corner, straining to see pictures in his head that were so far away they could barely be seen. The student was always alone his thoughts, and everyone else, far away. Paul's ethics professor walked by, not even noticing him. He was busy listening to a dialogue in his head. A male voice and a female voice, neither of them his own, were talking in muffled whispers about his marriage.

Some of what Paul heard and saw when reading peoples' minds was a bit like tuning into a distant television station. The pictures were hazy, nondescript, accompanied with so much static it was only possible for him to

make out a few words or images. People with this much static appeared dumb, but were actually internally deaf and blind. Some people talked to themselves so fast Paul could not understand what they were saying. From the look of confusion on their faces, they seemed to be clueless, too. People who looked grumpy or angry often had a loud, constant roaring in their heads, like many people arguing in loud voices at the same time.

Knowing *what* people said to themselves quickly became mundane for Paul, but hearing *how* they spoke was interesting and revealing. Paul discovered that people often assumed that whatever was going on in their head— loud voices, sounds too quiet to distinguish, static, repetition, bright or distant pictures—was also happening in other peoples' heads. Observing the variations in *how* people thought allowed him to know much more about them without getting tangled up in the web of *what* they were thinking.

As Paul followed Steve through the maze of tables, chairs, and incessant chatter, he did his best to block out the thoughts from other peoples' minds. In light of his recent experiences, he thought he was prepared for anything. Not so! He was about to meet a person who would change his life forever.

Steve's friend, Emily, sat at the table near the far corner. As they approached, Paul's breath caught in his throat. Sitting next to Emily was a strong-looking guy in a down vest and cowboy boots, and next to him was a Goddess.

Everyone has a weakness. Paul's was freckles and the smooth, light complexion that goes along with them. This young woman was freckled glory.

She may not have been everyone's idea of beautiful. Although long hair was "in," her light brown hair was neatly cropped short. About five foot two, she was obviously athletic, but not overly so. While everyone at the table chattered away with abandon, she sat quietly. She looked thoughtful, unwilling to talk unless she had something worthwhile to contribute.

Paul stared, struck speechless. He was drawn to this young woman like he had never been drawn to anyone before. Her blue eyes, bright against the soft freckles, riveted his attention. She was almost boyish, with her short hair and small breasts, but that was what Paul liked. If he could have ordered a romantic partner at a drive-up window, like a custom-made burger, she was exactly what he would have described.

Paul had survived the Hong Kong flu, his heart falling out, and spending a week with a dead person, but the impact of love at first sight turned him into a helpless child.

He tried to enter her thoughts, looking for a flaw, searching for some way out of this engulfing love. But he couldn't read her mind or anyone else's at that moment— he couldn't even read his own.

Steve was introducing Paul to the people around the table. Paul nodded weakly, his breath catching in his dry throat, as Steve pointed toward the Goddess and said, "This is Chorus."

Suddenly, Paul's view of Chorus was obscured by her flaw. The big guy in cowboy boots, standing up with his arm outstretched, was her boyfriend. He shook Paul's hand harder than he needed to, a warning perhaps, but he did not sit down again. He said a few words to Chorus and left for his next class. In what seemed like one of the luckiest moments of Paul's life, Chorus remained in her chair. As quickly and gracelessly as possible, Paul sat next to her.

Paul had never considered himself good at romance, but he was setting new lows with Chorus. He had never been smitten before. He could talk perfectly well to the other students, until he looked into *her* eyes; then he would be so overwhelmed he couldn't speak. Desperately seeking a way to ease the pressure, he surprised himself by moving closer to her. He was so terrified he wanted to run away, but instead he leaned over and whispered into her ear, "Marry me, please."

She smiled and whispered, "Not right now, thanks."

That was it. If he had not been hooked before, he was now. Paul's entire being tingled with warmth. It was a perfect moment. Paul smiled and wondered if this was heaven, with Chorus an angel. The Voice said, "Yes."

Paul reached for Chorus and pulled her to him. They embraced until a sound from the other room interrupted them. An infant was crying. Molly, their first-born daughter, needing some attention after a short nap. They moved into her room together. Chorus picked up their daughter and all three of them curled up on the front room couch as Chorus breast-fed Molly.

"Is this a dream?" Paul asked, floating in a haze, received no answer. "Am I reading my own mind, or Chorus'? Is this really going to happen, or is it only wishful thinking?"

When it came to love, there were no easy answers. Love turned Paul's clarity to confusion, and his confusion to an impossible muddle.

The conversation around the table had drifted from classes to camping. Paul, dazed and blinking, tried to pull himself together. Steve was launching into one of his stories about historical Gunnison.

"You know, our bank is famous! Only one in the west with special vaults."

The main vault had been built by a German locksmith. It was unusual in that it opened with a very intricate key instead of a combination.

The word "key" recaptured Paul's attention. He remembered the key the old rancher had left, seemingly by accident.

Now Steve was describing how the German locksmith had built five miniature vaults, smaller replicas of the main vault. These vaults were all privately owned but kept at the bank. They were on display, a local landmark used to draw people into the bank. The five miniature vaults were purchased by private individuals around 1880. Each one had been passed on from generation to generation, and there were plenty of rumors about what was in these special vaults and who owned them now. Like the antique main vault, the smaller ones also required very intricate keys to open them, but no one seemed to know who owned these keys. It had been twenty years since anyone had opened one of the vaults.

"Some say the last visitor to one of those vaults was a little girl with pigtails who found a key in her backyard, others claim it was a lumberjack who won the key in a poker game."

Paul reached into his pocket, and his hand closed around the intricate key. He looked at Chorus. She was listening to Steve with great interest

He leaned toward her and said, "Would you like to visit the bank with me? I think I have one of the vault keys."

She leaned over to him and said, "I would love to join you."

     Chorus and Paul left the student union together, but they did not make it to the bank that day, or the next day.

     Paul had once heard an old philosopher say that all he wanted out of life was "enough"—enough happiness, enough sadness, enough laughter, enough of everything. Paul was impressed with this philosophy, and decided to live a life that was good enough. After meeting Chorus, he realized that what he wanted out of life was "everything," and he would settle for nothing less. He would never compromise again, unless Chorus asked him to.

     Paul remembered the Chilean Fernando's lecture. "Without true love, one must muster all interest and moti-

vation oneself. With true love as a constant companion, every moment is doubly worth living." His words had made sense to Paul, but only as a concept—until he met Chorus.

Chorus and Paul went directly to his dorm room from the student union, eager to get acquainted. To Paul's surprise, they didn't speak much. Just being in each other's presence was a pleasure that words seemed to diminish. They had found a connection more intimate than words will ever allow. For two days they did not leave the dormitory. Without even sharing a kiss, let alone sex, they made love to one another. Dancing was as close as they came to expressing their love physically. They danced often during those two days. As a tribute to Fernando, they tried some seductive Latin dancing. Mostly they simply held each other while the music played.

They had each been starved for this love and had not known it. Their first evening together, the first supper, they ate potatoes boiled on Paul's camp stove and beans right out of the can. So much for a candlelight dinner at a fancy restaurant. Chorus laughed. "This is not what I expected to eat at the most romantic moment in my life! I pictured a fancy French restaurant, but this is much better."

Later, Chorus curled up in the same bed the old rancher had slept in the week before. Paul chuckled to see her small frame, like the rancher's, tucked under the covers.

He sat on the edge of the bed. "Would you like to hear a bedtime story?"

"Yes," she replied eagerly.

"Once upon a time there was an old rancher." Paul told the whole story, leaving nothing out.

Chorus smiled up at him. She not only believed his outrageous story, but appreciated it. It was a great relief to have someone to whom he could tell the story. She thanked him with her eyes as she whispered, "Good night."

Paul sat, hardly moving a muscle, and watched her sleep until dawn.

As she slept, Paul saw images of the skyline of a city unfamiliar to him. It was not much of a skyline. "A town desperately attempting to be a city," he thought. He looked closer and saw brewery signs and a lake beyond some tall buildings. "So this is Milwaukee."

Paul had been to Milwaukee as a young child. Now he knew he would visit it again. It was the hometown of his true love.

Now Paul could see Chorus as a young girl, pig-tails swinging along with the rest of her on a backyard swing-set.

Chorus had been a quiet, pudgy little girl. At the public school, other than being teased for her freckles, she was generally ignored by the other kids. Her father was

an alcoholic, and her mother a person "often wrong but
never in doubt." Somehow in this environment, Chorus
had thrived and gained something useful from every experience. During those first two days Chorus shared with
Paul, she ended several stories, positive and negative, by
saying, "In life, there are no accidents."

    Chorus had been molested as a child. When she
was twelve years old, her father sneaked into her bed-
room. He was too drunk to really know what he was
doing, and Chorus was too sober and tender to ever forget that night. From that moment on, Chorus had become
self-sufficient.

    "I will take care of myself, from now on," she had
said the next morning as resolutely as a twelve-year-old
can. A week later, when her father returned to her room,
he discovered that she was unwilling to be sexually abused.
She chased him out with an authority beyond her years.
Within a month her father had left home for good. For the
good of the whole family.

    To Paul's surprise, Chorus did not blame her par-
ents for her rough childhood. She thanked them. She
used her experiences as a young child to become dependent only on herself. Out of her adversity, and not because of it, she became strong and self-reliant. At an early
age, she developed an interest in art. Everything was art
to her: she saw art in Paul's shoes lined up on the closet
floor, she heard art in music and in the tone of Paul's voice,
and she felt art as she moved her body while they danced.

As Chorus spoke about her life, Paul shared her images:

Chorus as a child, making pictures in the sand along Lake Michigan. People pausing to admire her work as they passed by, complimenting her simple arrangements of sand and driftwood. Not the patronizing praise so many adults give children, but genuine praise. She seemed to inspire reverie and delight in all who looked upon her work.

Chorus enjoyed her natural gift at art, using it often, but never depending on it.

As she spoke, she built the story of her life for Paul, knocking down any possible walls between them. The important moments of her life were not the senior prom, her first date, graduating from high school, picking her college, or winning a scholarship award.

She recalled eating Chinese food for the first time. The strange tastes and textures inspired dreams of distant lands and people with thoughts and ways she could only imagine.

She shared with Paul a painting she had made in second grade. It showed a small town surrounded by a group of mountains, exactly like the mountains around Gunnison. The painting included a golden halo or ring above the town. Chorus had put the picture on her wall, and there it remained to that day.

The seemingly insignificant threads of Chorus's life wove a web that perfectly revealed the way the universe worked.

Paul listened to her words and shared the images in her mind.

He discovered that she never knew what she was going to say until she spoke, which kept her as interested in what she was saying as he was. She would see vivid pictures in her head, and artistically translate the pictures into words as she spoke. When she was not speaking, there was a silence inside her head. The quietness in her head was not slowness of mind, but peacefulness and calm. She was ready to remain quiet forever, or hear herself speak in the next moment.

During their two days of constant companionship, Chorus and Paul came to know each other in ways he had never experienced. The better he knew her, the more he loved her. When he'd first laid eyes on Chorus, he'd thought he was attracted to her looks, but the attraction ran much deeper than appearance. They belonged together. They both knew it.

Late the second evening Paul asked her about her boyfriend. "Oh, him. He was just a bridge who brought me to you." They had only known each other, or not-known each other, for a few weeks. She had helped him with his school work, and he had been grateful.

Although Paul was pleased to hear this, it did not really matter to him. He knew he would be in love with Chorus forever, no matter what she did or what happened. Each moment with her was a confirmation of their eter-

nity together, a reenchantment of the whole world, a reminder of what was important and good—love.

Love made a good life even better. This was not
just a love for Chorus, it was love for everything and everyone. Paul had always avoided romance novels, thinking they played on people's emotions without delivering
any satisfaction. Now he was living a romance, deeper
and fuller than anything he could have imagined. It took
him beyond his imagination, all the way to reality. Falling
in love, or rather rising in love, gave him a new perspective on life, but it was not a ticket to a life free from problems. Everything would not be smooth sailing from then
on, but everything would always be better for having met
Chorus.

Two people had entered Paul's dorm room on
Monday, but a couple emerged on Wednesday morning:
refreshed, hungry, deeply in love.

Paul smiled at Chorus and pulled the old rancher's
elaborate key from his pocket. It gleamed in the sun.
"Ready?"

She laughed and took his arm.

They were off to their adventure at the bank. But first, it seemed only fitting to stop at the same greasy spoon where Paul had eaten with the rancher.

The same waitress, serving their food, said, "How's the old man?"

Startled, Paul asked, "You saw him? You mean you really saw him?"

"Of course I did. Lots of college kids have their parents visit. But I never saw a father look at his son with such respect." Paul, blinking, remembered he had seen her at the airport the morning his dad left Gunnison.

As breakfast arrived, Chorus said, "Would you like to see what I can do?" Assuming Paul's "Yes," she set to work. Within two minutes she had assembled two works of art. On Paul's plate there was a piece of waffle cut to resemble a mountain, with an egg as a river running at its base and a group of hash-browns looking just like Gunnison. On her plate she arranged an abstract piece that inspired a soft whimsical laugh from Paul.

"You can do that with anything?" Paul stuttered.

"Of course," she said, without even a hint of pride.

They ate in silence, with the familiarity of a couple married fifty years, and the novelty of newly-found love. They ate a lousy meal arranged creatively, and enjoyed it. Love has a way of putting everything in perspective. Paul might have expected to hurry to the bank, anxious and excited to try opening a vault. But he was in no hurry. They had no schedule to keep.

Paul's relationships in high school, with family and friends, had been like a game of hide and seek. Now he was relieved to be found by Chorus, and had no interest in ever hiding again. He wanted her to know everything about him, to know exactly who he was.

Paul remembered his first "real" date and the missed kiss with Pat. This memory inspired him to remain observant. His relationship with Chorus would not be influenced by premature conclusions or judgments.

Paul would have married her the first day he met her, or given her the special key, if she had asked for it. She did not, and after breakfast they headed to the bank. Together.

The bank was like something out of a Western movie, bars on the teller's windows. There was dusty, rusted barbed wire strung around the walls, for decoration, and a musty smell. Paul presented the key to a teller who looked at the key, at Paul, at Chorus, then back at the key. In a serious voice she said, "You will have to see the president of the bank."

She led them to his office, a large, windowed affair, where anyone in financial need could easily be seen from both inside and outside the bank. Nobody could borrow money at this establishment without being seen. Mounted on the only solid wall in his office, to the left of his big mahogany desk, three heads of bighorn sheep glared down. The president, a heavy-set man bulging abundantly in the middle, leaned forward over his desk and extended his hand to Paul as they entered.

Shaking Paul's hand and ignoring Chorus, he said, "What can I do for you?" In cadence with his words was the thought in his head, "What do these kids want? I'll get rid of them as quickly as I can."

Paul smiled and did not respond immediately, leaving the president for a few moments to wrestle with the conflict between his superficial friendliness and covert hostility. Paul noted that being ignored had not bothered Chorus at all, and he decided to make up for the bank president's behavior by giving her more attention later. Standing in front of his desk, Paul slowly reached a hand into each of his front pockets, then pulled them out and held two fists out in front of him, indicating that the president should choose a hand. The president, a frequent winner at the Mayor's card game, said nothing and simply looked up at Paul. Not bluffing, Paul opened both hands, revealing the key in his left palm and nothing in his right.

The banker cleared his throat and dropped the pen he had been fiddling with. His manner transformed, he rose quickly and ushered Paul and Chorus to his leather sofa. He closed the curtains, turning his public office into a private den. He asked them if they wanted coffee, which they declined. Now he wanted to talk and know everything about them. There is nothing like the possible solution of a mystery to unite a person's superficial social personality and his or her genuine interest. The bank president's back sights had just lined up with his front sights. The target: Paul and Chorus. No, the key.

Clearly the rancher's key would open one of the special vaults. Although the bank president would have entertained Chorus and Paul all day, Paul asked to see the vaults.

The banker rose, indicating that they should follow, and led them to a room in which the vaults were prominently displayed. Every person in Gunnison knew stories about the private vaults, the bank's claim to fame. Speculation about their contents abounded. Over the years, the vaults' popularity and mystique had driven two other local banks out of business. Not even the promise of free checking accounts or toasters could lure people away from banking near the vaults, with their history and intrigue.

Every Fourth of July the bank sponsored the Gunnison Key Hunt by hiding fifty keys around town. The children of Gunnison and the surrounding area would spend the day searching for them. Each key brought back to the bank meant a shiny new silver dollar for the lucky finder.

This was not the Fourth of July, and Chorus and Paul were not here to collect a shiny new silver dollar. It was mid-March and they had a real key to a real vault.

The vaults were kept in a room easily visible from the street through a large, thick, barred window. Nobody was allowed to enter the room without a key to a vault, other than the janitor who cleaned the room once a month under the close scrutiny of the sheriff and two of his deputies.

Chorus was beaming, thoroughly enjoying the special treatment and excitement. Both of these paled for Paul in comparison to the honor of being with her.

Somehow Paul knew the key would open the middle vault. Fingering the elaborate curves, he eased the key into the lock and felt it click into position. Turning to the president of the bank, Paul asked him to leave them alone. Reluctantly the banker left the room, but Chorus and Paul were hardly alone. A crowd had gathered on the street outside the window—news travels fast in a small town. It had been twenty years since someone had come to the bank with a special key.

Paul whispered to Chorus, "Are you ready?"

She nodded eagerly and placed her hand on his shoulder, a gesture of familiarity that made it difficult for him to concentrate on the vault.

Paul started to turn the key, and the Voice said, "Stop."

Paul stood there, in the vault room with an audience of fifty people peering in at him, his true love's hand on his shoulder, and the key in place ready to unlock a mystery that might change his life. If the Voice had spoken a fraction of a second later, the vault would have been open.

Paul remembered the consequences of not trusting the Voice. While he was standing next to Chorus and the vault, he realized his purpose in life: to do the bidding of the universe and align his little world with everything that is, ever was, or would be.

Paul waited. Chorus, calm and trusting, waited beside him, more patient than he would have been in her position. Several minutes passed. Still they waited. Paul wondered what time the bank closed for the day. He pictured them standing there, key partially turned, forever. In his picture the crowd outside the bank increased for a while, then out of boredom the people began to leave. At first the picture seemed ridiculous, then Paul broadened his perspective, and suddenly the whole experience at the bank seemed purposeful. He realized that there is nowhere to get to and no such thing as waiting. If he never opened the lock, what difference would it make? If he never saw Chorus again, what difference would that make? It took him a few moments to realize that the vault did not matter. Chorus still mattered, until he remembered that if you hold too tightly to something, you lose the experience and pleasure of holding it. In that moment, he knew that he did not need Chorus and, instantaneously, he also knew that they would be together forever.

Paul tuned in to what Chorus was thinking. She was constructing a bit of art work in her head. She was doing so with a young child, a child from her future and perhaps their future together. The love and passion in Chorus's look reminded him of the way his mother had looked at him. As he enjoyed her thoughts, the Voice said, "Yes."

Paul finished turning the key in the lock and opened the vault just wide enough to see what was inside.

There was a silver-colored tray the full size of the interior, about ten inches square. On the tray were two large stacks of one thousand dollar bills. On top of them was a piece of old yellowed paper with numbers on it.

Paul had never seen a thousand dollar bill before, nor could he easily estimate how much money was in the vault. It was more money than he had ever seen—probably at least half a million dollars.

Chorus gasped. They both leaned forward to see what was written on the paper. There were two phone numbers, written in shaky handwriting, but legible. Paul memorized them. One number was local and the other long distance.

There was a startled cry. Chorus's hand slipped from Paul's shoulder. He spun bumping the vault door shut, and caught Chorus before she hit the floor, unconscious.

A gasp from the crowd observing them was loud enough to hear through the glass. The bank president came running. Paul, cradling Chorus, had only the presence of mind to grab the key. Appreciation requires a certain distance and perspective that activity excludes. Paul temporarily disappeared into his role, guaranteeing that events directed the next few moments.

The chaotic scene in the vault room struck Paul oddly like a well-directed movie, himself in the leading role. He was so busy, first with the vault and then taking care of Chorus, that he seemed to be outside his body viewing the bank scene.

The bank president produced smelling salts from a first-aid kit in his office. Chorus came to almost immediately. She was beautiful whether awake, asleep, or blacked out.

The banker stood over them, impatient to find out what had happened, but primarily interested in the contents of the vault. He was used to being in control. Paul and Chorus knew what was in the vault. They had the key to open it, and he did not. He was too nervous to even pretend to be gracious or friendly. He wanted to know what was in the vault, wanted to know it now, but was entirely dependent on them for the information. Surprisingly, being off-balance seemed to suit the banker—it did not make him attractive, but it at least made him less unattractive. He hovered over Paul and Chorus, unable to move or even think.

Chorus looked up at Paul and said, "Can we go?"

Paul answered, "Anywhere."

He helped her up and she leaned on him as they left the bank—to the protests of the president. A big crowd had gathered outside the ornate doors. Except for the annual Fourth of July parade, this was the biggest assembly on the streets of Gunnison since Teddy Roosevelt's visit many years earlier.

Steve and Emily were in the front of the crowd, next to a reporter from the *Gunnison Gazette.*

"What is in the vault?" yelled the reporter.

"Who are you?" the Mayor cried indignantly.

Chorus and Paul ignored the questions as they made their way down the street, escaping as quickly as possible. Steve and Emily stayed behind, talking with the reporter, who was willing to settle for information from a friend of the bearer of the key, since she couldn't get an interview with Paul.

"I've known him for a long time." Steve was launched.

The next day a picture of Chorus and Paul appeared in the paper along with a colorful story, one of Steve's better efforts. It did not start out with a dark and stormy night. Better, the story started with a prince in Germany, wandered through the foothills of the Prohibition and the Depression, and ended with wild speculation about the vault's "treasure." The story proved at least that Steve had learned *something* from college history and high school geography. The rest was imagination. The fact that very little of the story was true did not stop it from being read and embellished far and wide. As a result of the interest generated by his account of the incident, Steve was offered a summer job at the *Gunnison Gazette*.

Chorus and Paul fled back to his dorm room for peace and quiet. Paul held Chorus for well over an hour—close, tight, and warm. Finally Chorus spoke: "I'm sorry I fainted. I have never fainted before. It wasn't the money that overwhelmed me."

Paul waited patiently, enjoying each moment, knowing she had more to say. He had waited before, but never patiently. He continued to hold Chorus while he thought about the phone numbers on the yellowed paper in the vault. Neither number was familiar to him.

"The long distance phone number is the number at my mother's house in Milwaukee," Chorus said. "She still lives in the same house I grew up in. I have no idea how the phone number got there or what it means. It was just too much for me, seeing it there."

Paul could only stare. Finally he asked, "How old are you, Chorus?"

"Eighteen, going on five or fifty—it depends on the day," she said with a smile.

"If nobody has opened any of the vaults in twenty years, that phone number was put there before you were born."

They sat silently stunned.

They attempted to come up with some explanation for her phone number being in the vault. Chorus called her mother to ask if she had known anyone in Colorado back then. Her mother said no.

They were interrupted by a knock at the door. It was Steve asking if Chorus was all right, but really wanting to know what was in the vault. Paul told him he would know soon enough. Steve left disappointed.

Chorus and Paul finally deduced that the old rancher had put her phone number in the vault to make sure they would find each other. He had somehow known that Chorus and Paul were to be together, even before either of them were born. Which was crazy, but since they'd both come up with the same explanation intuitively, they decided to trust it.

Paul pulled out the key and stared at the elaborate convolutions of its design. He had learned that there were no accidents. The coincidences in his life were so far beyond his logical mind that it was easier just to accept them than to resist them or try to make sense of them.

The dead rancher had told Paul he'd let him know if there was a heaven. His time with Chorus could well be the answer.

"Child of Famous Rodeo Cowboy Seeks to Re-claim Gold," was the lead story in the *Gazette* a week after the initial visit to the bank.

It was time to call the local phone number. A young boy answered. "Howd on for a minute while I git my mom."

Finally, a sweet, down-home voice said, "Hello."

"You don't know me," Paul said, "I'm a student from out of town." He explained that he had gotten her number from a friend and had a message to deliver to her in person. She sounded pleased and gave him directions to her home.

Chorus and Paul went to visit her that afternoon. She lived a few miles west of town, the only house in a small valley. There were skinny cattle wandering free, and they had to wait for one of them to get out of the dirt driveway. Getting out of the car, they were greeted by three dogs with ten legs. Two of the dogs had three legs but seemed to get along just fine. The dogs, obviously not used to company, required a good bit of greeting.

The house, a shack made of leftovers and odd pieces from a lumber mill, had received more care than competence in maintenance. Though run-down, its newly repaired roof and varnished front porch railing showed that the owners kept it up as best they could.

They were met at the door by the smell of baking bread and a down-home smile. The plain-looking woman introduced herself as Jenny Tillson. Her hair was in a braid down her thin back, curly wisps of light brown hair framing her narrow face. Her features were angular, but her manner soft and appealing. Paul was just wondering how he would tell her about the phone number when Chorus and Jenny stepped past him into the house, arms around each other. Chorus, more talkative than Paul had ever heard her, was chatting with Jenny like a long-lost friend.

Paul wandered around the one-room shack. In the far corner was a bed that obviously belonged to the young boy he had spoken with on the phone. Opposite the bed was the kitchen. There was a small wood stove, a sink, and canned goods neatly arranged on shelves above a well-worn wooden counter. There was a fireplace with a small fire in it, and wood neatly stacked nearby. Paul took the liberty of putting a log on the fire as Jenny and Chorus talked on. He noticed a picture on the mantle.

In the photo, a familiar figure stood next to a young girl of about five. The girl's smile was the same as the one Jenny had given him a few minutes earlier. The man in the photo was the dead rancher.

As Paul picked up the picture, he heard Jenny saying her father was missing. She had learned of his disappearance from a neighbor. Though her dad lived less than a mile down the road, the only news Jenny ever got about him was from neighbors. Jenny explained that they had had a falling out and had not spoken to each other for twenty years. She could not even remember what the argument had been about. Over the twenty years, she had attempted to speak to her father several times, and had written him once a year, each time hoping she could reach him. Each attempt had met with no response. Now, with her father missing, she suspected that she would never have a chance to speak with him again.

"He always was a little different." He'd had a tradition of going for a hike each spring, calling it his "walkabout." He would disappear on foot into the mountains, and not return for a week. He would never warn anyone he was going, and when he got back he would act as though he had not ever gone. What he did on these walks was a matter of local speculation, but nobody had ever dared ask him.

This time Jenny suspected her dad would never return. He had been missing for three weeks.

Paul was still looking at the picture. He held it up and asked Jenny, "Is this a picture of you and your father?"

At that moment the door burst open and her son, Ben, entered with a smile. He was small for eight years, but carried himself with an energy that made him look bigger. In one hand he had a slingshot, and in the other he held a large jackrabbit by its hind legs. His mother and Chorus quickly set to cleaning the rabbit.

Ben walked over and stood next to Paul. Taking the picture he said, "Tat's my grandfadder."

He spoke poorly for a boy of eight though Paul understood him easily. Obviously he was more interested in hunting with a slingshot than in speaking well. Paul suspected he took after his grandfather in that.

They stayed for dinner, and it was almost dark when Chorus and Paul left Jenny and Ben. The boy had fallen asleep leaning against Paul by the fire. Jenny had taught Chorus how to skin a rabbit and cook one on an old wood stove. Chorus, comfortable learning new things, always made the teacher look good. The life she had just entered, in this shack, was very different from anything she had encountered in Milwaukee, but she'd fit in as if it was her own.

On the way back to the dorm, Chorus and Paul decided they'd like to be living in a cabin like Jenny's, with years of companionship ahead of them. They decided to help Jenny, and began to create an artistic plan.

By the time they got back to the dorm, they'd figured out exactly what to do. Paul wrote as fast as he could to keep up with Chorus's imagination as she rattled off a list of things that they'd need: "Two short pieces of rope, one harmonica, some dried beans, gray hair color..."

Often, the *way* something is done is more important than *what* is done. Paul knew they had to get the money to Jenny while preserving the mystique of the vaults. Gunnison had so little mystery it could not afford to lose any.

Paul called the bank president. By that time, the rumors were rampant around Gunnison, and the banker was impatient to have the vault opened.

Paul asked him to put curtains on the vault room window, and he reluctantly agreed.

The plan was well underway. Chorus and Paul headed for the hardware store and beauty shop. They had quite a shopping spree.

Over the next two days they completed their plan, including a dress rehearsal. In between preparations, they studied for final exams. Three days later, the bank president called and said the drapes were in position. Paul set an appointment for one o'clock the next afternoon.

The street in front of the bank was lined with people from Gunnison and college students, all hoping to get a glimpse of something extraordinary. Paul and Chorus did not disappoint them.

Paul arrived at the bank in filthy old clothes, a pick over his shoulder, toting a large cloth bag. He had dyed his hair gray and smeared it with old engine oil and dirt. He was wearing an obviously fake beard, knowing it mattered less what he looked like at the moment than how he would look in people's memories. He had done his best to look like the old rancher. His breath gave him a bit of added insurance that nobody would get too close. He had eaten several cloves of garlic and some Limburger cheese.

Chorus walked beside him, looking like she had just stepped off the pages of *Ms. Magazine*, wearing a business suit and carrying a leather briefcase. They walked into the bank as if they owned the place. This time the bank president did not know which of them to look at. Deposits and withdrawals at the bank came to a screeching halt. The town of Gunnison was officially closed for business that afternoon.

Paul and Chorus approached the bank president and showed him the key. He nodded to the sheriff, who was blocking the way to the vault room. The bank president followed them into the room, drew the curtains and promptly left—closing the door and leaving his odd clients alone in the vault room.

Chorus opened her brief case as Paul opened the vault. She pulled out some funny-looking contraptions she had made, all of them constructed to produce strange and wonderful sounds. She had a harmonica and home-made maracas, a tonette, and some tiny cymbals. She had an apparatus she had invented for this occasion, with fifty rubber bands strung across a small box. The bands, when strummed, produced fascinating pitches. For the next fifteen minutes, Chorus put on the strangest sounding concert the people of Gunnison had ever heard. There was not really a melody, but she was applying all of her visual artistic abilities to the domain of sound. The concert enhanced their performance, successfully encouraging rampant speculation on the street about what could possibly be happening in the vault.

Paul and Chorus wanted everyone to get their money's worth. His only job during the performance was to open the vault, put the money in his sack (leaving behind one bill), and locking the vault. Upon opening the vault, he was surprised to discover a small bag full of fine dirt where the paper with phone numbers had been.

He smiled and spread the dirt on the floor in front of the safe. To it, he added the rock chip from the rifle shot during his first campout. As he leaned the pick against the vault, he heard the Voice laugh: a melodious sound like a brook babbling, or a group of children laughing for no apparent reason.

Chorus looked at Paul. She had heard it too. They both joined in the laughter.

Chorus lit off a string of one hundred Black Cat firecrackers. The sheriff and bank president rushed in, and in the confusion of the moment, Paul and Chorus rushed out. The smell of gun powder, mixed with garlic and Limburger cheese, filled the vault room. Chorus took her chances with Paul's breath, kissing him on the lips as they ran for the door of the bank.

The crowd roared. Almost everyone in town was outside waiting, hoping to get a glimpse of a potential mythological character.

Steve, according to plan, had rented a hearse and was waiting half a block away. Paul and Chorus ran out of the bank, looking like an odd Bonnie and Clyde, feeling like Robin Hood. The crowd let out a collective gasp and parted as Paul and Chorus made their way to the hearse. Steve had covered up the license plate of the hearse, and his own face, with black makeup.

As they passed the *Gunnison Gazette* reporter, Paul imitated the voice of the rancher, saying, "I reckon anytime this many people get together, there ought to be a holiday." Chorus and Paul jumped into the back of the waiting hearse, and Steve drove away in a cloud of dust and smoke.

The next day Paul and Chorus returned to Jenny's farm. Jenny greeted them with a smile. Ben was out hunting.

"Did you hear about the old rancher at the bank?"

"Yes, we did. And that is what I need to talk to you about," Paul said, sitting down on the porch next to Jenny.

Paul told Jenny about her father taking him to the hospital. He described her father's death at the cliff.

"I knew it," she said through her tears. Though upset, sad to know for certain that her father was dead, she also looked relieved to have her suspicions confirmed. The three of them sat in silence for a while, and then Chorus invited Jenny for a walk. While they were gone, Paul placed all the money behind the picture of Jenny and the rancher on the mantel, with a note explaining that her father had left the money for her. He left the Remington single shot rifle under Ben's bed.

Chorus and Paul completed finals and readied themselves for a celebration: finding each other, completing their first year of college, and too many other things to mention. The celebration was to be a camping trip together, a weekend in the mountains, and perhaps their first sexual experience with each other.

Most of Paul's friends had been having sex in high school, or at least said they were. A large number of guys claimed they were having sex, but very few girls admitted to it. Obviously, there were more stories about sex than actual sex. Paul "kind of" lost his virginity as a sophomore in high school, "kind of" because, technically, he had just tried to have sex and never really accomplished it. He and Claudia had spent enough time trying, neither of them really knowing what they were doing, that he'd figured it counted as having sex.

After his initial failure, Paul had gotten a bit philosophical about the whole subject of sex, and was not interested in it strictly for the experience or conquest involved. What was important to him was the person with whom he would share such an intimate moment, not for

religious reasons or due to his upbringing, but just because he was very selective.

Paul guessed that he would have had sex in high
school if he had found the right person, but he had not.
He had now found that person, and he was feeling both
calm and excited about the upcoming weekend. He felt a
physical ache whenever he was near Chorus, or even when
he thought about her. It didn't really hurt, but it charged
him with more energy than he could possibly handle all at
once. He didn't want to just have sex with her—he wanted
to melt right into her body and join with her once and for
all, forever.

Paul could barely imagine what it must be like to
be an enlightened person. He suspected that such a person had sensations of connection with every person on
the planet, and probably with every animate and inani-
mate object as well. Chorus and Paul were so close that
they did not even seem to be separate people. Perhaps all
people are one and have to work very hard to maintain an
illusion of separateness.

This weekend was not to be about separation. It
was an opportunity for Chorus and Paul to enhance the
incredible experience they already shared. After the weekend, they would go their separate ways for the summer.
Chorus had a job lined up in Milwaukee, working with
children in a summer art-in-the-park program. Paul would
go back home and probably work as a land surveyor, the

same job he had held the summer after high school. He had not formalized his job plans, but his boss had let him know the job was his if he wanted it.

In spite of all he had learned, Paul was still trapped by society's expectations. It seemed strange that the social and cultural structures did not recognize his changes. He could go back to the same job as a different person, but he would be doing all the same things. It seemed that no matter how much he had grown spiritually and mentally, he was bound by the same cultural dictates as everyone else. He still had to work to earn money. Experiences, make people special, but they're seldom treated that way. Like many others, Paul was now confused about who he was, and how society could continue to misunderstand him. He could choose the typical solution—accept society's judgments and carry on with business as usual. Was that the right path?

Had Paul's education really only been eight months? It seemed like forever. Paul had come of age over those months, and what the future held in store for him he could only imagine. Only three things he knew for sure: his growth would continue, he would always love Chorus, and his life would always be worth living.

Chorus and Paul hiked west into the mountains. They traveled the shortest possible distance from town that would still ensure privacy. They found a group of boulders, clustered together, with an open flat expanse in the middle. This place promised the seclusion they wanted. The boulders overlooked a small valley with a view of both sunrise and sunset. They both knew it was the spot. They hugged and then rolled out their foam pads and sleeping bags.

Chorus and Paul embraced for hours while slowly undressing each other. Making love in the wide open spaces enhanced what was bound to be the high point of their lives so far. They spent almost the entire two days of their camp-out touching each other.

Chorus had a beautiful body. She was a bit of a tomboy, her breasts small and perfectly shaped. Paul knew that some other men liked large breasts, but he was not one of them. He tried counting Chorus's freckles, but would always lose track. He even tried counting the freckles on her right arm in hopes of later adding it to what he counted on her left arm, but again he lost track. He surrendered to the pure pleasure of immersion in his particular attraction to freckles. Hers were perfect.

They explored each other's bodies completely. Chorus was five foot two and Paul was six foot one, which meant they had eleven feet, three inches, and a lot of surface area to explore together. Even Chorus's feet were beautiful. Paul measured every part of her body with the corresponding part of his own. Her second toe was shorter than her big toe. She giggled when she discovered that his were the other way around.

"Our children's toes won't know how long to grow," she said.

Paul had learned much about his mind and body when they separated on the dormitory steps. Now he was learning about the unity of mind and body as they moved, thought, and breathed as one. This was a lesson that he could not have learned on his own. It took two open, willing, and loving people to discover pleasures too simple to imagine and too enjoyable to miss.

The first time they had sex was not distinct from their constant contact. Paul had often heard guys talking about having sex as if it was a separate event in life. It was not that way for him at all. Chorus and Paul were always engaged in cooperation, love, mutual respect, and admiration that made sex irrelevant and a great deal more pleasant than it was possible to express in words. Their moments together were constant foreplay.

Paul had waited for Chorus his whole life. Chorus had had a number of sexual partners before Paul. After her initial experience with her father, she could not take sex very seriously, or she would have been too upset by it. A culture that puts too much importance on sex presents a tragic scenario to anyone who has been sexually abused. Chorus had figured that out, and prior to this weekend, sex had always been an impersonal and unimportant act for her, not important enough to either avoid or engage in often.

This weekend was different. She was warm, alive, and every cell in her body seemed to be inviting Paul in— into her mind, into her body, and deep into her soul. He went gladly.

Paul felt tears of joy running down his face. Chorus slowly and gently licked them off. She smiled at him and whispered, "Thank-you." All thoughts disappeared and each moment heightened the ecstasy of the moment before. They moved together, they sang together, and they danced as one. The universe joined them, they vanished as individuals, and became everything. Niagara falls. The chirp of the tiniest cricket. A flower blooming in the rain forest, and a spotted fawn stretching for the first time. They expanded endlessly, rising, ever rising and descending at the same time. Lost and found in love, they entered a land of no borders or distinctions.

Finally, together, Paul and Chorus cried out. Paul heard the Voice give a sensual sigh.

The lovers were too happy and secure in each other's presence to be very upset by their imminent parting. As they dressed on their last morning at college, Paul watched Chorus, thinking of adventures they had shared. They had been together almost every moment since that first day at the student union. Paul was storing away memories of Chorus like a person stowing water for a trip through the desert. He put the key to the vault in his pocket, cherishing it as a constant reminder of Chorus.

Steve dropped them at the airport, casually mentioning his plans to marry Emily in the fall. It was just like Steve: he had not even told Emily yet.

Chorus and Paul stood together, glowing, not needing to talk. Paul looked around the airport at the other travelers. He tuned in to the thoughts of several people in business attire, but did not like what he heard.

What is it that allows children to play endlessly, while adults constantly act as if they must work all the time—heaven forbid they should play! Did life really have such a script for Paul? He hoped not. Then why was he allowing Chorus to slip away? It made no sense. She had quickly become the second most important person in the world to him. He was still the most important. He could live without Chorus—he had proven that for many years—but he did not want to. Why did it feel like he had no choice?

He had a plane ticket for home, and a summer job waiting. It would be irresponsible to change his plans now, though it seemed crazy to let Chorus go. Being spontaneous and following true love seemed irresponsible. He was caught. Paul wanted to be with Chorus, but had an obligation to return home: an obligation to himself, to his parents, but even more so to the consistency expected of an adult. Could being responsible really mean losing the person he loved, even temporarily?

Again he thought back over the events of the year. It had started with camping and ended with camping. In between had been more learning, happiness, and fear than he had experienced since he was a young child. As a young child he had grown and learned rapidly, but for some reason, as an adult he was not expected to continue that pace, nor was he allowed to. He was supposed to mature, which meant opting for security and consistency over growth. He was supposed to start showing off what he knew rather than continue to learn. He was supposed to know who he was, rather than create the person he could be.

Paul knew he wasn't the first to be caught this way—struggling between doing what he thought was right and doing what was necessary to become a "meaningful member of society." He was stuck on a sharp turning point in his life. He could play by the rules, or he could make up his own rules.

Beside him, Chorus stirred, and squeezed Paul's hand. She was tuned in to his thoughts and respected his dilemma, though she did not share it. Somehow, for her, things would just resolve themselves in the appropriate way. She trusted more than Paul did, and that was something he hoped to learn from her. At this time, a little bit of trust would go a long way for him.

He looked down at her. She looked up and smiled, giving him the trust he needed.

The man at the flight check-in announced the first boarding call for her plane. Paul said, "I love you."

She said, "I know. I love you, too. You will do what you do, and it will be the right thing."

He trusted her. She hugged him, kissed him, and walked out the door to the plane.

Paul stood staring out the door. He didn't know what he was waiting for. Suddenly the Voice spoke. "It's up to you."

Paul remembered his vow to never settle for less again, and in his head he heard the rancher say, "Heaven is what you make it, no more and no less."

He hurried toward the plane, knowing he would be getting on the right airplane with the wrong ticket.

As he climbed the steps to the plane he was greeted by a new flight attendant. It was the hug-prone woman Paul had met on his arrival in Gunnison. This was her first day on the job, and she was unsure of the rules. She stared, confused, at the ticket Paul thrust into her hands.

"I'm in love with a woman on this plane, and I need to go with her," he blurted out.

A broad smile broke over her face, and she let him on the plane. Paul caught her faint thoughts of Benny, and too many opportunities missed.

Chorus was sitting alone, tears streaming down her cheeks. Paul sat down beside her. She reached over and placed her hand in his, still crying, but now for joy.

About Jerry Stocking

Jerry Stocking is a modern day Thoreau living in the woods in Northern Wisconsin with his wife, Jackie, and children, Emily (7) and Judson (3). When he has something to write, Jerry commutes about forty feet from his house to his office. Jerry rises when he chooses (usually about 3:00 AM) and goes to bed when he wants to (usually about 10:00 PM.) His woods retreat has the latest computer equipment yet is unsoiled by television, alarm clocks, fast food or other vices so prevalent in the world. This atmosphere is conducive to the introspection so lacking in our fast-paced world. The children are living the freedom of being loved and cared for by two full-time parents and are being homeschooled.

Jerry hasn't always lived in the woods. He used to live in Milwaukee, WI and drive to work wearing a suit and tie. He was a successful financial consultant at Shearson Lehman Brothers. His past careers span the gamut of experience from owning his own retail stores to being an industrial designer to selling investments. All of Jerry's occupations have some things in common—he was successful at each of them and all of his job changes required a greater commitment to people and an increased ability to relate effectively with his clients and co-workers. Jerry loves people and is committed to finding out what is possible for "us" as human beings. His love of people and desire to contribute to them is apparent in his writing and lecturing.

Jerry is the president of a non-profit corporation, A Choice Experience, Inc., and a publishing company called Moose Ear Press. A Choice Experience, Inc. offers occasional workshops and a sixteen page quarterly newsletter, *Bridging the Gap,* which focuses on human possibility. The topics covered range from spirituality to personal growth to social commentary.

Jerry's credentials are impressive educationally, and even more so, experientially. A Master Practitioner of Neuro-Linguistic Programming (NLP), Jerry has been studying and using NLP for the past ten years. He has done extensive training in other-than-conscious communication and no-fault psychology. He graduated in 1974 from Northern Michigan University with degrees in psychology and philosophy. Though still learning and exploring daily Jerry has reached a point where he is ready to give back some of what he has learned in hopes that it will improve the quality of life for others.

Books by Jerry Stocking

Cognitive Harmony, An Adventure in Mental Fitness
There are No Accidents, A Magical Love Story
Introduction to Spiritual Harmony
Soon to be released, the *Spiritual Harmony Trilogy* and
Enlightenment is Losing Your Mind

Most people are mentally flabby. A few people are mentally fit. Mentally fit people produce more with less effort than their flabby counterparts. They enjoy life more and people want to be around them. They have better jobs and better relationships.

The book *Cognitive Harmony, An Adventure in Mental Fitness*, provides you with explanations and exercises in Mental Fitness.

Paul R. Sheele, MA, the chairman of Learning Strategies Corporation says, "*Jerry Stocking has taken a bold leap from analyzing behaviors and the structure of experience into describing the domain of consciousness. Delightfully, he has handled the leap adroitly. His blend of Neuro-Linguistic Programming and spiritual psychology gives personal growth aspirants a sturdy ladder to climb.*"

Hayward Allen of the Wisconsin State Journal says, "*The text is punctuated by drawings and a multitude of exercises to get into cognitive shape. This is definitely an introspective book. The reader is helped to develop expressiveness, perceptions and thinking patterns.*"

The sooner you begin reading *Cognitive Harmony, An Adventure in Mental Fitness*, the sooner you will be mentally fit and getting much more out of life.

Cognitive Harmony, An Adventure in Mental Fitness
$14.95 + $2.25 shipping and handling ($17.20)
Moose Ear Press   ISBN 0-9629593-0-8
PO Box 335, Chetek, WI 54728

𝕴ntroduction to 𝕾piritual 𝕳armony

Imagine that you are sitting across from God. What are your five questions for God? The answers to your questions may be waiting for you in **𝕴ntroduction to 𝕾piritual 𝕳armony**. What would life be like if you could celebrate and delight in waking, breathing, moving, and thinking?
How would life be if you could celebrate everything?

𝕴ntroduction to 𝕾piritual 𝕳armony
$7.95 + $2.00 shipping and handling ($9.95)

Moose Ear Press   ISBN 0-9629593-1-6
PO Box 335, Chetek, WI 54728

Contact Moose Ear Press, or A Choice Experience, Inc.
to find out about quantity discounts or information on other
books, tapes, seminars, or tapes by Jerry Stocking.

Moose Ear Press
A Choice Experience, Inc.

PO Box 335
Chetek, WI 54728

715-924-4906
FAX 715-924-4738